Daddy's Girl

Natori Pitts

ISBN # 978-1-7354621-8-9

PUBLISHING SERVICES
provided by High Maintenance Publishing & Production, LLC

www.highmaintenance1.com

"Providing Opportunities, Inspiration and Education to Independent Writers."

Filmmaker|Publisher|Author *Celeste Celeste*
High Maintenance Publishing & Production, CEO

4

Dedication

I would like to dedicate my first book to God. This journey was very personal. God broke me all the way down, but he didn't leave me nor forsake me. He put me back together and now I'm stronger, wiser, and so much better. God has been so patient with me; he knows my every flaw and still loves me the same.

When I felt fatherless, he put me in his arms and comforted me. During restless nights he gave me peace. When others spoke bad about me, he favored me. People changed on me and walked away from me, but he still stayed the same, he never switched up.

I wrote this book after being terminated from my employer, in the middle of a pandemic with not a dime in my savings. I was a lost girl with a story! This would not have been possible without My God he is my provider, way maker, miracle worker, promise keeper I owe it all to him, he is the real author I was just obedient and allowed him to use me. He gave me this book and now I'm giving it back to him!

Chapter 1

Growing up I heard lots of stories about my dad and the type of guy he was. From what I've heard he was solid, a hustler and a man of his word. He would give you the shirt off of his back. He was loyal to his friends and far too charming for just one woman. One of those women was my mother. He met my mom when she was 16, and he was just a year older. She was new to the neighborhood, the opposite of my dad who was well known around town. My mom was a young girl forced to survive on her own, trying to find her way in a new environment that nothing like she was used to.

My mom came from a decent lifestyle where her and her siblings went to church every Wednesday, Friday, and Sunday. They lived in a nice, gated community and attended private schools. One day their mom dropped them off in a town just 30 minutes from my dad's side of town and never looked back. My mom was bad standing bow-legged at 5'9 with a butter cream skin complexion and long black jet hair that passed her bra-strap, and it was all hers. People these days say that most pretty girls have big foreheads, but she didn't, she was petite with a long pretty face and a pointy nose. She had the prettiest white teeth, but she never smiled.

All the guys were chasing the new chick on the block, especially my dad. He had a dark skin complexion, average height with a round face and chinky eyes that stretched bucked wide when he was caught by surprise. His body was covered in hair, the one thing that ran in my family on both sides. It wasn't your average black hair either it was that hair that curls without even putting water on it. He was very versatile with his hair he would rock an afro, braids, twist or even cut it all off and it would grow right back.

My mom met a girl name Brenda at the high school she attended, and they became close friends, so close that they begin to call each other sisters. With her Aunt's permission Brenda welcomed both my mother and her sister into her home for the remainder of the school year. Brenda and my mom would get cute in their best outfits and walk the streets. They would walk to the neighborhood called the tank, it was called that because it had green tanks that people would sit on, play cards on and hangout around.

The tank was my dad's hood where he grew up. My mom would watch him from afar. What attracted her to him was that he was different from the other hustlers out getting money. He didn't have a body full of tattoos, a mouth full of gold teeth, nor did he carry himself like a thug. He could walk in a club full of flashy niggas with designer on, gold chains, popping bottles, and catch everyone's attention by just dressing casually, and being himself. He would make noise without speaking. Most men chased women, but he was being chased. He chased my mom though. He would see her in the tank with her friends while shooting dice and making plays. He would stop everything he was doing to get her attention. He begged her friends to hook them up.

After a long chase, my mom gave in, and she became his #1 girl. During the time they were dating he was always in and out of detention centers. One day he escaped from one of the centers and broke her virginity, and sure enough my mom became pregnant with me at 18. I was made while my dad was on the run. I was an escape baby, at least that's what my parents called me.

A few years went by and my dad's money was getting longer, and his name was getting even more respect in the streets because he wasn't selfish, he wanted to see everybody eat. When it came to my mom and I we didn't want for a thing.

My mom was in the hair salon every week, she kept a full set of nails on, and was always dressed to impress.

We went from living with his grandma to living in our own apartment where she had it decked out. I had every pair of Jordan's that came out and every toy in the store. Every day was Christmas for me. My dad filled my neck and wrist with jewelry. We were spoiled and we had the best of everything. Although I was really young I remember the bond my dad and I shared. I remember, I was about 2 years old laying on his chest as he tried to put me to sleep so that he could leave without me knowing. I would always cry, holler and screamed when it was time for him to go. I never wanted to leave his side. I would be sound asleep, and he would come in the house late at night trying his best to tip toe past me, but I would jump up every time. See he thought it was because he wasn't being quiet enough but what he didn't know was I felt his spirit the moment he was on his way home. I can't explain it, but I just knew, and I would wake up and pretend to be sleep until he walked through the door, and I was always right. Within a few minutes he was pulling in the driveway.

One day he left and never came back home. I stayed up waiting all night. No matter how late he walked into the house after partying, running the streets, or kicking it with other females I knew he was coming home, but this time he didn't. I cried myself to sleep that night. My dad broke my heart for the first time at just 3 years old.

He was picked up by the feds on drug charges and was accused of a homicide. My mom would go visit my dad in the local jail before they shipped him off to federal prison. One particular morning my mom went to visit my dad, she got dressed in a pretty red Tommy Hilfiger dress my dad bought her, it was tight fitted, with the matching shoes and purse. When she got to the front desk to sign in she noticed another woman's name on the list for the same time. She looked over at the screen he was supposed to be showing up on and seen another chick sitting there. She waited until he showed up on the screen and charged towards her. She snatched the phone and asked him what was up and to make her leave. He said no. She flipped out and called him all types of fuck niggas and pussy niggas, everything but a child of God.

"I got 100 hoes and you ain't one of them!" He yelled back.

My mom looked him in his eyes and told him that if he gets a dollar from every last one of his hoes he would have $100 in his canteen and fuck him because he would never have to worry about her ever coming back to see him again, and she didn't. My dad was sentenced to 17 years.

The first 5 years of my dad being away I never saw his face again besides on pictures. We talked on the phone a lot but that was it. We were back living with grandma because we couldn't keep up with the lavish life we lived when my dad was free. Life became harder for us all. It wasn't just us two anymore. My parents had two boys after me. Three kids and my mom didn't even own a car. My dad left us out here stranded with nothing but material things that were no longer any good.

Chapter 2

I was 8 years old when my mom finally let us visit our dad. She didn't take us herself because we didn't own a car, and she couldn't drive anyways. She kept her word of never visiting him again too. I know deep inside she still loved him she was just fed up and tired. Maybe him going to prison was her escape to heal from all the times he hurt her. I never seen that part of them I was too young. To me, my dad was an angel and could do no wrong in my eyes. I still felt like that even while visiting him in a cold prison.

My uncle drove us to Atlanta, Georgia on our first visit. Not only was it our first visit but it was our first road trip. I was excited and nervous. I kept asking my uncle how much longer and each time he answered saying that we were almost there. For the first time I begin to feel butterflies. When we got to Georgia I remember the hills and feeling like we were on a roller coaster the way the car was going up and down each road. We passed by huge homes that were sitting high on a hill with long driveways. It looked like you were on one of those rides at the theme park waiting to go up in slow motion just to get to the house. I could only imagine how the ride felt going back down. It was about 50 degrees outside, but it was upsetting that there wasn't any snow in sight. Once we got to the prison I was in awe. It looked nothing like the prisons I saw on TV or what I'd envisioned from people who talked about it. This prison looked like a museum. It was more like a mansion built from old brick that was surrounded by tall stainless-steel fences.

Once we entered the gate, security was waiting for us, after that we parked and approached a large stainless steel double door. We were buzzed in and immediately greeted by 5 officers who were managing the visitors as they walked through a metal detector. My hair was in a side bun, I remember having to remove the pins because they were activating the alarm. I was looking a mess, but I didn't care.

After the metal detector we put our items in the lockers and sat to wait in a cold waiting room. We sat patiently as the guard called the next crew of visitors towards the back. When the guard came inside the room he called us by my dad's last name. We lined up and followed the guard through another double door. Once we got through the door we were back outside in the middle of two gates that we had to stand between for about 10 minutes as we watched another crew of visitors walk by us going towards the exit door.

When we got inside there were 5 more guards walking around the room, 5 vending machines and a photo booth. I watched as inmates sat with their family engaged in conversation. I started to shake from being so nervous and the butterflies in my stomach were back. The guard showed us to our seats, and we all sat quietly looking at the door in front of us where the inmates came out one at a time, each in tan jumpsuits and black boots.

The clock seemed to move so slow and the room started to spin as I sat nervously looking at the door hoping I would be able to recognize my dad when he made his entrance. Staring at the door this man walked through the door with braids going back wearing reading glasses, before I knew it I jumped up and ran to him and jumped in his arm. We held each other so tight as we walked back to our seat.

During the visit we laughed, talked , and took multiple pictures. For the first time in 5 years I felt at peace. I felt protected in his presence. I was able to be Daddy's little girl again instead of the oldest who had to do everything back at home. Visitation was only an hour. We were down to our last

15 minutes and I began to cry I didn't want to leave my dad I wanted him to come home. He gave me a forehead kiss and told me that he was coming home soon and to be patient. He told me that no matter where he was he would always protect me and love me and not to worry about anything. I believed him I had become confident. We told each other *see you later* and I watched as the guards led him to the exit door to line up with the rest of the inmates. While the visitors walked towards the exit I sat and watched my Daddy walk away until I couldn't see him anymore.

Back home it was the usual. My mom was always working or out with her boyfriend. Most of the time she would leave bright and early in the morning, and we wouldn't see her until dark or the next morning. My mom was still young and since my dad was no longer in the picture, and she had finally got on her feet to be able to get us our own place I felt like she was trying to play catch up with her life. Which meant taking away mine. When she was gone throughout the day I was responsible for looking out for my younger siblings. I learned how to use the stove and whip up something really fast for us to eat. I made sure they took baths, and their room was clean before she got home because she didn't play the radio when it came to her house being messy.

I was surprised when she let us get a dog. Polo was a mut that we found wandering the streets one day walking from the corner store. He almost got hit by a car in traffic. We saved him and tried to go our separate ways, but he followed us home and refused to leave. We didn't want him to leave, but we knew our mom would not let us keep him. I guess he was just too cute to give up, so she gave in and said yes. Polo was white with brown patches covering his fur. He had brown eyes and droopy ears. He looked so innocent he became family to us. My siblings and I loved that dog, we would play hide and go seek with him in the yard. We would hide from him and call out his name, he would head straight in our direction, full speed with his ears flapping in the wind. My brothers and I would split up and take off running, it was like we were running for our lives because Polo was extremely fast and sometimes too aggressive.

We didn't go to theme parks or summer camps, so we made our own fun while being home alone. We climbed trees for fun, our tree had gotten so big and the branches were so strong we had found a way to get on top of the roof of our house by climbing the tree and holding on to a branch that had fallen on the roof. We would walk around the roof of the house with no shoes on throwing sticks at each other like straight Bay-Bays kids. Of course my mom wasn't at home when all this was going on.

When my mom would leave us home she always had our neighbor check in on us. They were cool people especially Mr. Matt he had a big crush on my mom but that's all it ever was his old ass didn't stand a chance. He was an old dark skin man who had a bald spot on the top of his head and had missing teeth his whole front grill was gone it was funny because he would always be chewing and I never knew exactly what he was chewing so hard since he didn't have teeth, later on I found out it was something called tobacco that he would chew and spit out. It was disgusting. Matt always had a beer in his hand and in the other hand he had money he would give us to go to the store with. He would load us in his pickup truck and take us to the store with him and let us rack up on all type of stuff we had no business getting. Even though my mom taught us not to be around strangers and not to play around men Matt got a pass because he had been our neighbor for a while. He was a good dude who always looked out for us.

One weekend my mom was home, and she had her friend girls over. They were all sitting outside on the porch talking and

14

drinking wine coolers. My brothers were in the road playing football, and I was in the house alone taking a bath. John, this guy who I had seen my mom talking to 2 weeks prior, introduced his self to us as our cousin, he explained how he was our cousin on my dad side and how if we ever need anything to hit him up because he lived only 2 streets away. He was telling my mom how he was a handyman and could fix almost anything. That was all my mom needed to hear since my brother had broken the window in the house and it needed to be repaired.

I don't know why she just didn't ask Matt.

John showed up that day to fix the kitchen window. As I was sitting in a tub full of bubbles playing with Sasha, my Bratz doll head washing her hair, the bathroom door slowly opened. At first, I thought it was my mom coming to tell me to hurry up and get out the tub, but it was John. He was tall, bright skin with braids and a baby face. He was much older than me, but he definitely wasn't as old as Matt he had to be at least 25. Once I realized it wasn't my mom I yelled out loud that I was using the room. He peeped his head in more and then walked in.

"Sorry lil cuz I got to pee."

As soon as he said that my heart started beating fast. He had ignored me and invaded my privacy. I barely knew this man, and he was looking at my tiny naked body like an animal hunting his prey. I was shaking so bad I couldn't speak. It was like he was staring a whole into my body with his demon eyes as he grinned.

He walked towards the tub put his hands in the bubbles, the next thing I feel is his hand on my vagina! I jumped and tried to scream but I got choked up. I could literally hear my own heart beating.

He put two of his fingers inside me. It hurt so bad I felt his nails scratching the inside of my walls. I had never been touched like this before. I was only 8 years old. I hadn't even started my period yet. As the tears begin to run down my face, he looked at me with an evil smile, he was sick and possessed. He walked quickly out of the bathroom. Once he left I was finally able to breath again. I began to cry.

I jumped out the tub, dried off, put my clothes on and headed outside where my mom and her friends were still sitting around laughing. When I got outside, I noticed he had already left. I walked over to them and just stood frozen.

I've heard people talk about how women and girls who don't *speak up* or wait weeks, months or even years to mention these things are liars or it's because they really wanted it. Until it's you or someone close to you that has gone through it, you will never know how hard, scared, embarrassing and emotionally depressing it is to speak up not knowing what's going to happen next.

"Girl what's wrong with you? Why are you standing there looking like a zombie?" My mother asked.

"Ma… John touched me"

"What? What do you mean he touched you?" She screamed.

"I was in the tub, and he walked in after I told him I was inside. He came into the bathroom anyways and put his fingers inside me."

My mom jumped up.

"That's why that motherfucker was rushing out of here so fast." My mom went next door to get Matt. He was the only man around to defend us. It's crazy how a neighbor was more of my family than my so-called cousin.

They headed up the street in Matts pickup, straight to John's house while my mom was on the phone with the police. I stayed back at home with my little brothers. Minutes later my mom and Matt were back with the police, they needed to ask me some questions. My mom assured me that she believed me and that he was going to jail.

John wasn't at the house when the cops got there. They couldn't find him. I was so hurt and confused I didn't understand why my dad's cousin would do this to me. I couldn't wait until my dad called so that I can tell him. He broke his promise, he told me that no matter what he would protect me, but it was a man, who claim to be his cousin who hurt me. I begin to feel hurt and betrayed by my dad.

People in jail get the news on the streets quick. They find out things quicker than the news because within an hour of the incident my dad called and all I heard was my mom yelling through the phone with tears in her eyes I couldn't catch the whole conversation but within a few minutes she called me over and handed me the phone.

"Daddy?" I whispered into the phone.

I heard his voice so calm. I knew him like the back of my hand, he was livid, but he would never let me see him sweat.

"Hey beautiful how are you feeling?

"I'm sad daddy can you please come home. When are you getting out ?"

"Soon baby but until then daddy is going to make sure you are okay and safe. I promise nobody will ever hurt you again. Daddy has everything under control. Now let me ask you something you can fight right?"

"Yes. I beat up my brothers all the time."

He laughed. "Well keep fighting, but not your brothers. You fight anybody who tries to do something to you or look like they want to try you. I told your granddaddy to bring you a pocket-knife he's going to show you how to use it. I know you have a little purse to carry, put it in there. I'm going to have your Mom give you some pepper spray too. You and your brothers always stick together no matter what. You are a beautiful princess in a wicked world, but daddy got you forever. I will always protect you."

It's bizarre how I went from feeling betrayed by him to forgiving him and believing that he was really able to protect me from prison even though he had been proven wrong.

"You have 30 seconds left." The operator said in the middle of our conversation.

We exchanged I love you's and after the phone hung up I no longer cared about that monster because I had so much faith in my daddy. I trusted his word again. Word on the street was John's family secretly moved him out of the state and I never heard about it or saw him again.

Chapter 3

I was now in the 6th grade, and I was no longer that chubby tom-boyish girl anymore. I started getting my nails done and wearing hairstyles other than braids and beads like weave ponytails with the hump, twist with waterfalls and cramps. Although I had really long hair I loved to wear weave from time to time to get new look. I was at Fisher Bay Middle School. The bus ramp and hallways were always lit, almost everybody in the West Brooks community who shared the same school zone went there. It was a new school that had just been built and we turned that thang out. We took over the nice 2-story building with the big eagle mascot that sat on the top of the entrance doorway.

Every morning I would meet my boyfriend at the bus ramp. We had to sit on the bus until the school security gave the bus drivers the okay to let us out. Once I was off my bus I would wait on the bench until I spotted him, and we would walk into school together. Jaylen and I started dating after a few weeks into the school year, it was clear that he really liked me because from the first day of school he always picked at me and followed me through the hallway. We had every class together, so it was hard to avoid him.

One day in 3rd period while Mrs. Allison was going over our math homework Jaylen passed me a note. I opened it... *I like you! Do you like me yes or no* ? I laughed out loud because I never expected It because he was so arrogant and loved to act hard in front of his friends. I apologized to the class for my outburst from laughing out loud and circled yes and passed the note back to him. His face looked puzzled since I was laughing he didn't know what to expect inside the note.

"That's what I thought, and you better call me tonight" he said after confirming my selection.

Jaylen was so cocky, but I knew there was another side of him that he was hiding. I was willing to give him a chance despite his mean ways. Later that night I called him, and we hit it off quick. We fell asleep on the phone together. Before I knew it, I was Jaylen's girlfriend, and it was official. I was his girl and the whole school, them lil' groupies that followed him around in the halls, and his football team knew what was up.

Jaylen played for the Wildcats he was number 21, and he was good. I would rock his jersey every Friday and strut the school halls. A bitch couldn't tell me anything. I was proud to be his girl. We would spend every weekend together after his games. He lived with his grandfather, just the two of them. My mom would drop me off on the weekend after his game, and we would hang out for the rest of the day. His Grandfather was a nice man. He was short like Jaylen with a dark complexion. He didn't look that old in age maybe because he didn't have any wrinkles, but he did have a gray beard and a bald head that he always hid under a ball cap. He had a deep voice that sounded really aggressive when he spoke to other people but when he spoke around me, it was gentle and calm. He always looked forward to me stopping by.

When we hung out at the house he would always tell us to keep the room door open and absolutely no kissing or touching. Jaylen and I were both still virgins and never thought about doing it. At least not until we started hanging out at my place.

My brothers and I were always home alone and had way too much freedom compared to other kids. My mom would tell us there was food in the fridge, not to mess up her house and then leave. My mom was too busy out dating this new guy she had just met. When my mom thinks that she found the one it's no stopping her, she was always on a mission. She really didn't care what was going on at home. My brothers and I would have all our friends over every weekend, our place was always the hang out spot. Jaylen was over more than anybody spending time with me and playing the Xbox with my little brothers.

One day my mom dropped me and Jaylen off at the house after picking us up from early dismissal and then left after saying she would be back in a few. We were home alone! After hours of talking about school and football, watching him play the video game, and play fighting we both laid on my twin canopy bed that was covered in all pink silk sheets and turned a movie on. Jaylen begin to give me a hickey on my neck something he never did but it felt good, and I was beginning to feel moist between my thighs. I was hot and ready.

We begin to tongue kiss and Jaylen slowly unbutton my jeans and slid them off. We both were breathing extremely heavy and my heart was beating so fast because I couldn't believe that we were really about to do it. I was so nervous I didn't know anything about sex my mom had not sat me down just yet and talked to me about it. I just knew Jaylen heard each beat through my chest probably thinking I was being dramatic; he was a smart ass and always had something to say. Once my pants were off, he began to take my panties off while we were still kissing with our tongue down each other throats. He started to rub on my bare pussy lips. I got even more moist. I was wet as a rain puddle. I widened my legs for him cause at this point he was teasing me, and I was curious to know what else he had to offer.

He began to play with my clit making circular motions then flicking his finger really hard against it causing my clit to cry

21

out for more. I never experienced this feeling before, but the way Jaylen was caressing my clit had me questioning If he was really a virgin. He started to finger me. I jumped and stiffed up trying to ignore the thoughts of when I was touched in that way without my consent. Before I knew it Jaylen pulled his pants and boxers off and begin inserting himself into me. He was so excited that he shoved it inside me hard instead of being gentle. He began to penetrate my virgin pussy while moaning like he was in heaven, but he was the only one enjoying it.

It hurt and felt like a burning sensation inside me, I was hoping he would slow down and take his time, but I was too scared to speak up. I thought maybe I didn't know what sex was about, and maybe this was how it was supposed to feel. He grunted loudly in my ear and begin to slow down he quickly jumped up, and he emptied out his dick on my silk sheets. I laid there looking at the ceiling through my canopy as he walked out of the room to wash himself up. I heard the bathroom door close and the water run. I quickly got up to put my clothes back on because I was insecure about my body and a boy seeing me naked. As I got up while moving the covers back I noticed that my sheets was covered in blood, my cherry popped! I was 12 years old when I got my first piece of dick.

When my mom returned home the first thing she did was ask me what was on my shirt. It was blood. I tried not to look guilty by changing only my pants thinking she wouldn't notice because I still had the same shirt on. I lied and told her it was a ketchup stain that I spilled while eating some fries I had made for me and Jaylen, and she really believed me. Thirty minutes later Jaylen's grandad was outside beeping the horn, and he left.

The next day in school in P. E class while doing my daily stretches on the floor in the middle of the gym a boy name

Cliff walked past and asked me "How did it feel?" He was laughing and I was confused as fuck.

"What are you talking about? How did what feel?" I asked him.

"Getting smashed for the first time!" he blurted out hysterically.

Cliff joked about Jaylen telling him and some other boys how he smashed and took my virginity. I was so hurt! How could he betray me? I ran into the girl's locker room and cried my eyes out. I wanted to talk to my dad and tell him because he promised me that nobody would hurt me and here I was hurt again, and this time with a shattered heart. I knew I couldn't tell him because I had no business fucking anyways, and he probably would look at me different, I wouldn't be Daddy's little girl anymore.

Shay was in the locker room. She was an 8th grader, mixed with white and black she was very pretty with freckles in her face. She had long curly red hair. Shay had wide hips and a big butt for her age. All the boys in school were on her trail. She always had a new hair due every week and a new purse, she stayed to herself in school she never talked to anybody she just walked the halls with her nose tooted up. She was changing out of her PE uniform when she saw me crying like a lil bitch. She walked over to me and said she knew why I was crying because everybody was talking about it in the cafeteria at the lunch table.

"Girl that's why I don't fuck with boys my age because they childish and don't know how to act when they get some pussy." She said while tying her shirt up in the back as if she wasn't going to get in trouble for violating the dress code.

"My boyfriend is in high school he has his own car and money these lil niggas could never get the time of day they disgust me." She continued.

I just stared and admired how pretty she was and how she carried herself it was something about her that was different than me. I knew what it was she had a real man in her life, and I had a lil boy. From That day forward I told myself I would never talk to a boy my age again. I took Jaylen back after I dumped his ass because it was hard to just leave him he was my first boyfriend and my first, for the first time I felt loved by a male other than my dad, for the first time someone called me beautiful other than my dad, held my hand and told me they loved me other than my dad, who was no longer around. After a while Jaylen started cheating with other girls on the cheer team and in school and even then I still stayed. I was young and learning how to accept and tolerate a man's bullshit just to feel loved. Jaylen began to get a little too cocky and got kicked off the football team and started getting into trouble in the streets. He went to jail for 21 days and I broke up with him. I wrote him a long letter with tears in my eyes I was tired, and I was over the relationship. That was it for me call me what you want but I left and never looked back.

Chapter 4

Now that I was in the 8th grade my clothes begin to get tighter, my boobs got bigger, and I was feeling myself. I was the lil red baby with the long hair on the block that everybody wanted. The boys my age didn't get any play, I had learned that lesson. In my town we started having club events for teens called the Baby Club. It was always swole, everybody came out to hang out. Most of the time it was held at the skating rink called Raymond's on Saturday nights. My friends and I would get dressed in our best outfit and our parents would take turns dropping us off.

On this particular Saturday I was really feeling myself I had just got my belly button pierced, and I was ready to show it off, so I put on my purple and black dickie outfit. It was a black shirt that said dickie on the front in purple letters with some purple shorts with my customized name plate belt. I had on some fresh all black Reeboks with purple fur ball socks. My shirt was tied up so that everybody could see my new piercing. I had a long 26inch weave ponytail in my hair, and I brought out all my jewelry from the gold bangles going up each arm to the big dolphin gold plaited necklace and matching earrings. I was the shit, and couldn't nobody tell me I wasn't.

All the cute boys were out, so I had to be on point. The ages for the Baby Club were 13-17 so when me and my friends got dropped off after getting our wrist band and paying our $5 we went straight to the high school section with the older crowd. We always got there late because when the club first opens the first hour everybody skates, and then they turn the floor into the dance floor later that night. My girls and I liked to find our lil corner to stand in and just vibe to the music.

Grind With Me by Pretty Ricky was playing through the speakers and all you could hear was everyone singing the lyrics, word for word. Me and my girls was rolling our hips and trying to see who could touch the floor the best and get back up. When it came to dancing I was a pro I picked up fast on every new dance that came out I was the friend who starts a dance battle in the club. Across from me, I noticed this really tall skinny boy staring at me and smiling showing all his gold teeth. Back then the boys had pull out golds. At first, I thought maybe he was looking at someone else but every time I turned in his direction, his eyes locked with mine. He was kinda cute and I could tell by looking at him, he was a little older. I pretended like I didn't see him staring as I continue to dance with my girls. *Get Low* by Lil Jon played, and I was crunk. As I was dancing my friend tapped me on the shoulder and gave me a piece of paper rolled up I looked at her confused, and she pointed at the same guy still staring and smiling at me. She said he walked over and asked her if I had a boyfriend, and she said no, so he wrote his name and number down. I was really dancing hard not notice they were having a whole conversation behind my back. I stuck the number in my pocket and played like I wasn't bothered but deep down I was happy and couldn't wait to hit him up later.

I was talking to other boys, but it wasn't serious. I had a hard time falling for a guy like I had fallen for Jaylen we were together for two and a half years, he was all I knew. I had told my older cousin about the guy at the club, and she told me not to call him if he wanted me bad enough he would find a way to reach me, so I threw away the number. A week went by and Austin Jones sent me a friend request on MySpace it was the same boy from the club. I accepted the request, and it wasn't even a minute before he sent me a message.

*Damn lil baby what happened to you calling me you
went missing on me, I must be ugly, or you must got
back with your lil boyfriend ?*

I was wondering how in the hell he knew I used to have a lil
boyfriend, but then again Jerome was a popular football
player, so it was obvious. I was so tired of being known as
Jaylen's girl. I was ready for something new. We talked back
and forth and finally; I gave him my number. I was halfway
through 8th grade, and he was a sophomore in high school.
We started off as friends who talked on the phone all the time
and seen each other, but we weren't having sex.

Right in the middle of the school year my family moved to a
new house and I switched schools. I was now at Palmer
Middle School, and I was the new girl. It wasn't hard for me
to fit in because most of the kids I was familiar with I either
knew them from the club or the football field. I was the class
clown and was always in timeout for insubordination. I was
not the pretty girl with good grades and manners. I didn't give
a damn about school; I was just there for a fashion show and
because I had to go. It didn't take me long to feel like school
was a waste of my time. I had clicked up with these 2 girls
Amber and Taylor, and we used to skip class every Friday. We
would go to school and wait until third period and leave out
the back gate. Palmer Middle School was right in the middle
of a neighborhood and it was an outside school that was only
secured with a metal fence that anybody could jump over. The
plan was to be back by 7th period which was the last period of
the day so that we could get on the bus and be at parent pick
up on time as if we were in school the whole time. We had it
down packed.

When we left school campus we would walk to the store and
meet up with the high school boys since they got out of school
early. We just hung out and had fun. Until one day we skipped

class and Amber wanted to meet up with a guy she had been talking to she said he was going to meet us and pick us up. Something told me this wasn't a good idea, and we should just keep hanging out with the high schoolers like we always did. We had a routine that I wanted to stick to, and I wasn't trying to get caught, so I told her I was going back to school, and she said it was okay he was going to drop her off home.

Taylor and I went back to school and when I got home the school had called my mom saying Amber's mom was looking for her, she never made it home. I was so damn mad cause now she was about to get me in trouble and my mom would find out we had been skipping school. The principal told my mom that they checked the school cameras and seen us leave out the back gate together. Later that night Amber finally answered her phone and told her mom she was at a hotel I had no idea what she was doing at the hotel, but she had the whole school and my mom thinking we were skipping school and getting fucked but birds of a feather do not flock together in this case. She had turned something that was supposed to be just chilling until a big thing that had caused all three of us to get suspended and had the nerve to beat me being mad because I didn't want to be her friend anymore. She was on some shit that I just wasn't on.

The rumors had started, and I was known as one of the little girls who skipped school to go fuck boys. My name was drug through the mud. I found myself fighting on every corner trying to clear my name. My dad would call from prison and give me these long speeches.

I ended up skipping school again with another friend name Daphne she said she was going to get some money from a boy she was talking to for school lunch and it would be really fast. I agreed because I was just that type of friend down for whatever, but I already had it in my head that this was going

28

to be the last time I was doing this as if I didn't already get my ass whooped by my mom. We walked to the boy house and It was 2 guys one was dark with braces and long dreads and a Puerto Rican boy with long straight hair. I started to get that feeling again that something wasn't right. We walked in the house and I sat on the couch with the Puerto Rican boy looking dumb because we were supposed to just come get some money and go back to school. My friend walked in the room with the other boy and closed the door. While I was in the living room the boy was trying to hit on me, and I was giving him the cold shoulder. After about 10 minutes I heard the headboard knocking and moaning. I instantly got mad as fuck. I did this girl a favor by coming with her, and she lied to me, she came for some dick not money. I refused to get caught up in this shit again, so I told the boy I was leaving and going back to school and to let her know that I was gone. I may have seemed like a bad friend for leaving her but fuck that I got tired of getting myself in these situations and I wasn't even the one getting dick.

The Puerto Rican boy, Kanon, offered to walk me back to school. He seemed nice once he realized I wasn't giving in to whatever he thought was about to happen. We walked and talked most of the way. Before we went our separate ways he looked me in my eyes and told me I was different, at first I was offended so I rolled my eyes at him, but he said no it's a good thing. He said there was something about me that made me different from the rest. He said I didn't seem like the type of girl to hang out with someone like Daphne. I thanked him for walking with me, and we went our separate ways.

I made it back to school just before the bell. I headed to parent pick up where my mom was waiting on me. The next day in school it was obvious my friend was mad at me for leaving her, and she started saying lil slick shit in class. We were in Mr. Williams math class. He was a really nice teacher the only

29

teacher where I felt like he actually cared about his students. I tried to ignore her little side comments, but she was sizing me and doing a little too much.

"Listen bitch I ain't tell you to go get fucked for some money, so I left." I blurted out.

The whole class went crazy. Mr. Williams told both of us to stay in class after bell rang. We both sat there as he tried to make peace with the situation, but she wasn't trying to hear it, and I was on whatever she was on, so he let us go and warned us that if it happened again we would be in the detention room for a week. At the end of the school day I was walking one of my other friends to her bus on the ramp before I headed to parent pick up. I noticed a crowd of people coming my way with Daphne leading the group. Her hair was tied up and her jewelry was off I guess she wasn't going to let the shit go from earlier in class. I already knew what time it was I didn't have time to take my book bag off or jewelry off, but I was definitely not about to let her get the first punch so before she could say a word I hit her and the face, and we went to fighting.

I couldn't believe I was throwing punches at a bitch I thought was my friend all because I left her and I didn't want to be a part of what she had going on. Here I was suspended again this time it was for the rest of the school year because she was bleeding. She only got suspended for 3 days because her dad was the computer tech at the school it wasn't fair but at an early age I was learning that life wasn't fair at least not for me.

I barely made it to high school I was failing all my classes but thanks to Mr. Williams he was able to help me catch up with make-up packets to complete during my suspension. It was the beginning of Summer, and I was still talking to Austin from the club and now that I was becoming a freshman in high school we started to get serious and make it official. Austin was so different from Jaylen he was more mature, and he took his time with me. It wasn't long before I fell head over heels for him. Austin turned my lil ass out. He showed me where all my hot spots were and had me doing different positions during sex he had my nose wide open. Couldn't nobody tell me anything about Austin I was in love, sprung and addicted to him. Austin didn't have a car or a job, but he was old enough to drive, so he would come pick me up in his mom car. He never bought me anything, but he didn't have to, he had bought me with all the shit he was doing to me, he had my head in the clouds.

I had changed my MySpace name to Mrs. Jones (his last name) and had Tynisha Keli *Me And You Against The World* playing in the background. Everything was so good until I found out he cheated on me and had a baby on the way. I thought my heart was broke from Jaylen, but Austin broke me all the way down. I cried for weeks because I wasn't only competing with another girl I was competing with a baby. I was the one that should've had his baby. I had our whole future planned out; it was supposed to be me. I was devastated. My mom told me I was too young to be somebody stepmom and I was forced to break up with him. It was crazy that even after all of that I had to be forced to leave him I still wanted this boy. I had become weak and vulnerable why was I like this when it came to boys why was I so desperate for love and affection. I found myself falling for anything.

Chapter 5

It was the end of summer, and I was trying to mentally prepare myself for high school, but I just wasn't feeling it. I didn't pay attention in school and thought about dropping out every day. I knew that my mom was not having it as long as I was in her household. The only class I loved was English because I loved to write, that was the only class I passed with an A. Other than me hating school it was hard for me to focus when I was so caught up with Austin the whole summer. I was trying to get over this boy and I couldn't. Even though the baby turned out not to be his he still went and started dating another girl, it was like a slap in the face. I went from being the one he cheated on to the one he cheated with because I would still sneak around with him. I figured a piece of him was better than not having him at all. I was lovesick, and I hated it sometimes I would lay in bed and pretend to be physically sick so I wouldn't have to go to school. This particular morning I lied and told my mom I wasn't feeling well so I could stay home she never argued with me, she said okay and went about her day. It was only the first semester and I had missed over 10 days of school. I would sit home and do chores around the house and just chill.

On this particular day My mom called and told me to go get my little brother from the bus stop because she wasn't going to make it in time. I didn't mind, it was only one street behind us. My brother was in first grade, so we didn't let him stand at the bus stop or get off the bus alone. I brushed my hair down in a wrap, threw on some jean shorts and a burgundy top with my black slides and headed out the door. I was halfway to my brother's bus stop passing a house that was full of guys standing outside talking. One of the guys with dread locks yelled out to me.

"Damn lil baby how old you are ?"

I pretended not to hear him and kept walking, but that didn't stop him.

"How old your fine ass is?"

"14 why?" I blurted out with an attitude because he was so ugly.

"Damn you mean but that's okay you too young for me anyways "he said, and they all started laughing.

I rolled my eyes and kept walking. Once my brother's bus came, and he got off we headed back home, so I could help him with his homework. I hated that I had to walk past the house again with all the guys but this time they didn't say anything I guess my age scared them away.

I noticed a silver Durango backing out of the driveway with two of the guys inside. They slowed the car down as I was walking and a bright skin guy with glasses rolled the window down on the driver's side, but it was the guy on the passenger side that was smiling at me. He signaled for me to come closer to the car and I did. He was brown skin with pretty lips and a bald head. He didn't look my age, but he didn't look old either. He didn't have any facial hair his skin was clear and smooth like butter, not a scar or bump in sight.

When I walked to the car he smiled showing the prettiest white teeth I have ever saw he asked me where I was headed, and I said home. He asked if my brother and I wanted a ride and I told him no, we were just the next street over and I didn't get in the car with strangers, he was tickled by my reply. He told me that I looked familiar and asked me who my kin people were. I told him my dad's name because it seemed as if everybody knew him, I told him my mom's name too, he didn't respond like I thought he would, he acted as if he never heard of them. He asked for my number and said he would text me from his homeboy phone until he got time to buy a new one because he had just got out of jail. I gave him my number and headed back home.

The rest of the way home I thought of Austin. It made me sad because I hated the way he had me so gone and flaunted his new girlfriend in my face all on MySpace together. I needed to get over him and if giving this guy my number led to something I was down I was going to show Austin that two could play that game.

The next day I got a text message notification from a number I didn't recognize.

Hey, it's Eric the guy from yesterday.

I text back hey, and he called me. He was funny I loved his sense of humor I was anxious to see him again, so he told me to meet him at the same spot we met at, so we can hang out. When I got there he was in the same car with the same dude driving. When I got inside the car I looked at both of them and asked why he was here. They both laughed.

"I'm his personal driver cause the nigga license suspended, and he's scared to go back to jail."

We all bust out laughing. We ended up at this park that was just built so it was still nice and clean, meaning the homeless people hadn't started taking over yet. The driver stayed in the car on his phone while we walked to the park and talked. I asked him why he went to jail, if he had a girlfriend and how old he was. He said he had a few drug charges, and he had just broken up with his baby mother. He told me he was 17.

"Stop lying you have kids and a baby mother I know you have to be older than 17."

He changed the subject, but I didn't really think anything of it. I liked him, honestly, I didn't care how old he was. Time went by, and we were talking more but seeing each other less. He always had an excuse every time I wanted to see him, he claimed he was busy, and that he would make time for me. He finally got tired of me complaining once I told him I was done, and finally pulled up on me while I was at my friend's house.

For the first time he wasn't in that truck or had his lil personal driver with him. He pulled up in a Buick that was dipped in purple and sat high on 22' inch rims. My friends were looking out the window in awe trying to see who this guy that was coming to see me. I was smiling from ear to ear saying to myself, *damn this a big upgrade from Austin that nigga ain't have no car but my new boo got a car a nice ass car*. I knew it wasn't gone be long before I got over that nigga!

I used to hear stories about my dad when he was out in the streets how he had nice cars with nice paint, big rims playing music through his loudspeakers and TVs. I could only imagine, but here I was experiencing it firsthand. He didn't stay long but once again I was looking forward to seeing him again and again. Fuck school and fuck Austin I wanted to be under this guy all day every day.

The following Monday morning I was getting ready for school, and he sent me a good morning text, making me blush. We text back and forth, and he asked me what I was wearing to school and did I want to stop and get breakfast before my classes. Clearly this nigga was a drop out or he really was lying about his age. *A nigga taking me out to breakfast before school, hell yeah that's lit!* I wore my beige dress with sunflower prints, I flat ironed my hair into a nice slick ponytail because he always talked about how he loved my long pretty hair, slid my foot in some pretty gold sandals and headed out the door where he was waiting. I yelled out to my mom telling her I was gone, and I shut the door behind me, she never came out the room.

He wasn't in the nice car, he had the truck this time, *damn this nigga keep switching up cars* I said to myself. We stopped at Fowler grill, when we pulled up it had a white female mannequin standing in front facing traffic with a bikini on and I thought it was hilarious. When he parked the car he told me to wait so he could see who was inside before we entered, which was weird like he was trying to hide me or something, or he was hiding from somebody.

During breakfast we talked and laughed the whole time I felt myself really falling for him. He flirted with me the whole time making me blush. After about 30 minutes he tipped the waiter, and we left and headed to my school. We ended up arriving earlier than I thought, so he parked across from the school in an apartment complex and said he would wait with me until the school opened the doors. We sat in the car and chilled and was play fighting when he grabbed my hair and my rubber band popped. I was mad and hit him.

"Now how I'm supposed to go to school with my hair all messy." I laughed playfully.

He laughed and said he would find me another rubber band. He got out of the car and walked over to my side and opened the back door then handed me a brush, He stopped a man who was walking by and ask him did he have a rubber band and to my surprise he pulled one out of his pocket. That was the sweetest thing to me!

I fixed my hair, and he opened up my door and grabbed me by my hand. I got out of the car, and he hugged me as we stood there holding each other. He made his way under my dress and felt how wet I was and started laughing. It was funny because I didn't even realize I was wet; I was just caught up in the moment. The nigga smelled so good.

He pushed me inside the car and laid me on the seat and pushed my panties to the side. I could tell he was excited because he was moving really fast while unbuckling his pants. When he inserted himself into my tight, wet pussy he made a loud moan and within a few minutes he had came, just that fast. Out of all the times I've had sex, this time was different. I was more than sure that he had nutted in me.

We both got up slowly and it was like an elephant in the room we didn't say a word to each other. He got out the car fixed himself and hopped back in the driver seat. I stayed in the back getting myself together, and he drove me to the front of the school. I got out of the car and walked away as if I was in a hurry to get away from him.

"Damn you ain't gone say bye or nothing." He yelled out.

I turned around and waved and headed inside the school looking for the girl's bathroom. Inside the bathroom I took off my wet sticky panties rinsed them off and tried to dry them as much as I could with the hand dryer. So many thoughts were going through my head, *will I ever hear from him again now that we've had sex, did he care that he nutted in me, did he even realize, what if I got pregnant, no fucking way I'm going to get pregnant,* I kept telling myself. The bell rung and I headed off to class.

When I got home from school I rushed into my room, closed the door, and text him. I had so much on my mind at school I couldn't focus, as if I gave a damn about school anyways. He called once he saw my text, and he seemed normal. He asked how my day was. I asked him if he noticed that he nutted in me. He got quiet and said not to worry because he knew for a fact that he pulled out. I argued at him letting him know that he didn't, and that he was really tripping.

He hung up on me and my heart dropped in my stomach. I begin to cry. I was hurt I couldn't believe he was acting like this towards me, I couldn't figure out what did I do to him.

Every day I called his phone, he ignored me,, my calls and my messages, and each day I was getting sicker and beginning to have a bigger appetite than normal. In school during lunch I would eat all my food especially the cheeseburgers, it was crazy because I never ate school lunch, but those cheeseburgers were like a steak off the grill. I ate mine and I ate my friends who was looking at me crazy.

A month had gone by and I notice my period didn't come and it was only a matter of time before my mom noticed too because we always got our period on the same day. My mom always bought our pads and feminine items, so I was wearing them pretending to be bleeding and cramping from periods when really it wasn't a spot of blood in sight. I began to get nauseous and my breast begin to hurt terribly. I was miserable, so lost and confused. *How am I going to continue to hide this? Why am I being treated like just another hoe to Eric? Why did he change all of a sudden?* I knew I was pregnant from all the facts I read while googling my symptoms the only thing I was missing was a pregnancy test to really confirm what I already knew maybe then Eric would come to his senses.

I asked my grandad for a few dollars and asked if he could take me to the dollar store for some supplies for a school project. I purchased 2 pregnancy tests and waited until the

39

next day in school to take them in the bathroom. Both pregnancies test came out positive. I cried hysterically, my world was beginning to fall apart, and I didn't know what to do. I couldn't afford an abortion, and what was I going to tell my parents?

Later on that day I tried calling Eric again after the third try he finally answered. He sounded so unconcerned and mean like I did something wrong when all I wanted to do was talk to him.

"Hello?" I said softly.

"Yeah wassup?" He answered non nonchalantly.

"Eric why have you been ignoring my phone calls?"

"I've been trying to make it work with my baby mother and I have been busy" he said.

I started to cry again he asked what was wrong.

"Eric I'm pregnant I took two tests today."

"...and what that got to do with me? I'm not the only nigga you been fucking I heard you was a hoe."

I stopped breathing and the phone dropped. I began to feel dizzy; the room was spinning. I tried to make it to the bathroom in the hallway, but I couldn't. I vomited all over the floor. I sat there and cried. I needed somebody but I had nobody to run to. I cleaned up the vomit, got in the shower and cried some more. I cried so much, I slept like a baby and didn't wake up for school the next day.

When I finally did wake up, I had text messages from Eric telling me to call him. I called, and he apologized telling me to give him some time to come up with some abortion money. Funny how I was so intrigued by this man who I thought had his shit together, and his ass couldn't even pay for an abortion. I hung up because I was tired of hurting and crying, tired of hiding this secret and lying, tired of tossing and turning every night, and I was starting to feel kicks in my stomach that caused my mind to be all over the place. All my friends were hanging out, and I was home depressed with nobody in my corner.

I text Eric and told him that I was going to tell my mom about the pregnancy in the morning. I got no reply. Hours later he called me on three-way with someone and started yelling in the phone calling me a lying bitch. He started accusing me of lying about my age and saying I told him I was 18 and how he showed his people a picture of me, and they told him who my parents was and how if he had known who my dad was he would have never messed with me because they grew up together.

I was confused as to why he was on the phone playing victim and why he has someone on three-way with him lying saying he didn't know my age. I begin to feel sick to my stomach, this nigga was really trying to turn this all around on me. All I heard through the phone was him calling me names telling me I'm a liar and to never call his phone anymore. He even pulled up my MySpace where it said I was 18. That meant nothing because you had to be 18 or older in order to make an account. I didn't meet Eric on MySpace we were never friends on it, so I couldn't understand where all this was coming from why he was making me seem like the bad person when I told him everything about me in the beginning, and he was okay with it. He hung up on me again.

I was so tired of crying and feeling hopeless and empty inside. I don't think I've ever cried so much in my life I cried until I

41

had no more tears left. I stayed up all night trying to figure out how I was going to tell my mom I was pregnant without involving Eric because he clearly didn't want anything to do with me or the baby and I still didn't understand why he was acting like a victim and bringing up my age and my parents, he acted so scared when I was the one that should be scared. I thought we were in this together I was beginning to be very overwhelmed. As I sat up in the middle of the night trying to figure out how to tell my mom I was pregnant I came up with what I thought was a brilliant idea.

I text Austin and told him I was pregnant, and that I was almost 4 months. I had to tell him I was further than I was so that he wouldn't question it because if he was to add the months up with the last time we had sex it would be impossible. Just like I imagined he didn't question me and was ready to support me through whatever once I told him the news. I explained to him that he shouldn't say anything yet because I haven't told my mom yet and I needed time, and he understood he was so understanding.

That morning as I nervously walked to my mom's room I was so scared I knew that at any moment I was going to shit in my pants. When I got to her room she was laying down on the phone gossiping as usual. I asked if she could get off the phone because I had something to tell her.

"What girl why you come in here bothering me and why aren't you in school?"

I just stared at her for a minute, it amazed me how I stayed in the same house as her and was going through one of the worst times in my life, and she didn't even notice, not one time. I began to cry again.

"What is wrong with you girl?" She yelled.

"Mom I haven't been having a period and I think I'm pregnant."

"I know you a motherfucking lie, stop playing because we get our periods together you just had a period!" She yelled.

"No mom, I lied I'm not playing, I believe I'm pregnant."

"Well we about to go to the Doctor and find out right now and if you are imma beat it out of you."

On our way to the Doctor my mom called at least 10 people it was already hard enough telling her and now she was spreading my business all over the town. Parents like to say kids don't have business, but they do, and it hurts when your own parent tells it. Not once did she ask me if I was okay or how I felt.

At the Doctors I was asked to pee in a cup, and I was asked when my last period was. After answering the questions the nurse left out of the room and returned within 5 minutes. Congratulations Sweetie you're going to be a mommy. I started to cry again not because I was happy but even though I had already known it's like her calling me a mommy did something to me. I was 14 years old and I had nothing not even the baby daddy. My mom looked at me and said it's from Austin right? We need to call his mom you all need to figure out what you all about to do because you can't stay with me with no child I got enough damn kids as it is.

On our way out of the clinic she called Austin's mom and told her the news then she got on the phone again and started telling everybody how we just left the office, and I was really pregnant she kept going on and on and on, and I was beginning to hate her. She had no idea what I had been going through this past month, but I really couldn't blame her.

43

On our way to my grandma house I begin to feel terrible about the lie I had made up about it being Austin baby I was due for an ultrasound the next week, and he was going to figure it out that the baby wasn't his I felt bad. While my mom was running her mouth on the phone I yelled to my mom to please get off the phone.

"No bitch" she yelled back, "You don't tell me what the fuck to do with your hoe ass, done sat up here and got pregnant. Your life is about to be fucked up; you're supposed to be better than me you're actually worse! Hell when I got pregnant with you at least I was 18, your ass only 14. April your life is fucked up. Congratulations."

"Mom please get off the phone I have something to tell you!" I screamed out with tears in my eyes. She hung up the phone.

"What?"

"Austin is not the father!"

"Well damn you just a hoe. Who else you been out here fucking? Do you even know who the father is?"

I begin to cry because I couldn't believe the way my mom was dogging me; she was no better than him.

"Eric!" I blurted out.

"Who the fuck is Eric?"

I showed her a picture, and she hit the brakes hard, almost causing the whole car to flip over.

"His name ain't no motherfucking Eric that's Mike, and he is a grown ass man! Did he force you?" She screamed and begin to speed like a bat out of hell.

I was flabbergasted I couldn't believe this boy I was falling in love with lied to me about who he was. He knew who I was the whole time is that why he gave me a fake name? He pretended he didn't know my parents when he actually did, and they were around the same age. He was 29 years old, there was a 15-year difference with us. I even found out he is my brother's cousin, on my dad's side. Is this why he began to act so mean and weird once I told him I was going to tell my mom about the pregnancy? Is this why he called me on three-way with someone yelling as if he was the victim? I begin to feel rage through my body I felt hate. This is the second man to prey on me who knew who my dad was and knew I was his daughter.

"April did he force you?" My mom screamed at me again.

"Yes he did." I replied. She began to cry hysterically while flying down the street.

When we finally got to my grandmas where she immediately called 911. Before I knew it I was being questioned by cops over and over again they kept asking me the same questions. Within 24 hours the word had got out, and I was the talk of the town.

Some people were calling me a hoe and saying I was fucking so many niggas that it could be anybody baby. His family was trying to meet with us and talk to try to convince my mom not to press charges. Eric/ Mike even offered to pay us if we didn't go to court. I looked on MySpace and the people who I thought was my friends was talking about me. I was on this fake page someone made about me being the biggest hoe in town. I was devastated since the moment I told my mom I was pregnant the situation got worse I regretted everything even being born. Austin called me and to my surprise he wasn't angry or mad. He actually called to tell me he was sorry about what was going on, and that he was glad his name was cleared. I never heard from him again.

I was ashamed to go to school, so I would pretend to go then sneak back in the house after everybody left. I tried to kill myself, but I failed at it each time. A week went by and it was time for the deposition. My mom and I pulled up at this big, tall, black building with people all around in suits and ties. I waited in this area where a detective greeted me and told me that I would be asked some questions that I already answered, and it would be quick. I nodded my head and followed him in the back.

There was a room with a round table and at least 8 people sitting at the table staring at me. I had already been through enough and I had started to get exhausted from all this court and police stuff. I tossed and turned for nights concerning the lie I told my mom about Eric/Mike forcing me. As bad as he did me and all the bullying I was going through I just couldn't go on with the lie anymore I needed some type of peace in my life so as they went around the table and asked me the same questions over again this time I told the truth. The sex was consensual and that he never forced me. I never lied to him about my age and that was the Gods honest truth. I had nothing to lose, my name was already being slandered, I was being bullied, I was 3 months pregnant, and I was starting to believe my mom when she said my life was really fucked up.

Later on that day I had to face something that I was dreading, talking to My Dad! I knew I was no longer Daddy's Little girl after this, and it made me feel even more worthless. When I spoke with him on the phone at that moment all my hurt vanished it was like he was the missing piece that I needed all along. Every time I spoke with him, he gave me hope he made me feel like I could conquer the world. He spoke so softly as he reassured me that he would take care of it and that I wasn't having the baby I was going to have an abortion, and he would send someone over to give me the money. He and my mom argued about her decision to get the police involved he claimed to have had a better idea but whatever that was my mom did not agree to and wanted to make sure men like him pay for what they did in jail. It was and still is a trend for older men to sleep with younger girls or if they get caught they pay the parents not to say anything. My mom looked me in the eyes and told me that no amount of money would make her turn on me, and she had my back. For the first time through all of this I felt relieved that despite my mom shortcomings when it came to defending me she was always in my corner ready for whatever no matter what people said.

Erick/Mike was still denying the baby and going on with rumors about me lying and him not knowing how old I was and who my people was. I had tried my best to ignore and block out everything that was going on, but I was beginning to go into deep depression. One early morning I was brushing my teeth and I began to cramp really bad and the room started to spin I had become dizzy. I fell to the floor with a sharp pain in my stomach. I felt weak, so I yelled out to my aunt who had just moved in with us. She came into the bathroom picked me up and laid me on my mom's bed, but the pain kept getting worse and I felt like I had to poop so I asked my aunt to help me to the bathroom.

Something didn't feel right with my body. As I sat on the toilet and begin to push I screamed out in tears because it hurt so bad. Blood was everywhere with huge blood clots. I cried for my aunt to call my mom who was at work. My mom explained that I was having a miscarriage and not to flush the

47

baby. I was becoming weaker and my body got extremely hot I had never felt pain like this. When the pain eased up a little I was able to stand up a little I looked inside the toilet and seen my baby. It had legs, feet, toes, fingers, lips, nose and eyes. I've never seen anything like this in my life.

My aunt put me in the shower and began to clean up. My mom had arrived and told me we had to go to the hospital to make sure I was okay. She had gloves and a tube that kinda looked like the one the nurse had me pee in for the pregnancy test. I watched her as she used it to scoop the baby up out of the toilet and squeezed the top close. She said she was doing what the detective asked her to do. The baby was considered evidence for DNA.

Having a miscarriage didn't make me feel any better I was becoming more suicidal and nobody noticed. I would wait until everybody was asleep and I try to force myself to stop breathing. I took a whole bottle of pain pills so that I could overdose but nothing happened. I didn't have a reason to exist I had no friends everybody hated me, and I was failing school. It was getting closer and closer to the actual court date where I would see Eric/Mike for the first time since he took me to school that morning. It's crazy how just a quick minute can change your whole life.

The night before court my mom had called me into the room she said that she was about to do my hair in some little girl ponytails, I looked at her like she was crazy. She said that it would help at court in front of a jury to see that I'm just a little girl because they will try to judge me off of my appearance and say I didn't look my age. I started to cry because this shit sounded ridiculous and I didn't understand. I asked her if we could just forget about court and not show up because I was tired of the backlash and I knew that once he went to jail it would only get worse, but my mom was determined to put him

48

in jail. I sat between her legs as she did my hair in ponytails with pink hair bows at the end and knockers. I was embarrassed I just wanted all of this to be over it was too much for me to fathom. I didn't have a voice; nobody knew what I was going through or feeling. I needed help I was becoming mentally drained I didn't know who I was or where I was in life.

I found myself at that tall building again. My mom and I met up with the public defender, and she explained to me how I would possibly have to take the stand my legs began to shake it was no way in hell I was getting in front of a jury. I had been through enough I turned around and told them I was done, but my mom told me, it wasn't up to me. I didn't have a choice and the public offender nodded in agreement. My heartrate increased and I just knew I was going to have a heart attack before I entered the double doors to the courtroom. We walked in the courthouse and I saw his family sitting down giving me the nastiest looks. The public offender took her place in front of the judge, and we sat behind her. A lot of legal talk was going on that I didn't understand I was spaced out trying to forget where I was.

My heart dropped when I saw him walk in with cuffs on he had turned his self in when everything first hit the fan. We made eye contact. One part of me felt hate in my heart for this man because of the way he played me and made me out to be the bad guy and manipulated me. The other part felt bad for him because I really liked who I thought he was. My emotions were all over the place. I heard him agree to a plea of 15 years and was charged with lewd Lascivious Battery, Sex with a victim between 12 and 15 years old. That was the last time I had seen him, but it wasn't the last I had to hear about it.

Chapter 6

The first thing my mother did after court was take me to the Doctor to get put on birth control. She had to find out I was fucking the hard way, and she wasn't willing to take another chance and neither was I. I had changed high schools to get a fresh start as I entered my sophomore year. I was looking at my report card full of F's with only 3 credits. My school guidance counselor had already made it clear that there was no way I was graduating unless I went to a virtual school and even then it didn't mean that I was going to graduate on time. Most guys who tried to holla at me backed off once they heard I put a man in jail. My name was tarnished I looked around and the friends I used to have were gone, I couldn't call on them any more everything and everybody was changing right in front of my eyes. I didn't see any hope for myself I was useless.

I went to visit my dad and it was depressing, usually I'm happy and excited, but I was starting to feel like it was pointless. Seeing him gave me false hope and temporary love, I felt safe and secure with him but that was only for an hour then I was back outside in the real world with no guidance. I praised and worshiped the ground this man walked on. I was bragging on this man who I was starting to feel like was causing me so much pain and hurt. The illusion of him some day coming home and being Superman was taking over my life and it was causing me to be vulnerable. I was looking for someone to fill his shoes, and looking for someone to love me like he did and spoil me and call me princess like he would. Every time he wrote me a letter it would always start off with, 'What's up my beautiful princess?' To me that's what I thought I was, a princess.

During visitation, my dad told me something that gave me hope again. Every visitation I would ask him when he was coming home, and he would always say very soon, as the years kept going by it seem as though soon was far away and never coming. This visitation was different he told me that he would be home to see me graduate I knew he wasn't just talking because he looked me in the eyes and pinky promised me that soon was getting really close. It had already been over a decade I was only 3 when he left me and here I was 15. I was the happiest girl alive at that moment. I had something to look forward to but on the ride back home it dawned on me that I would fail my father. He would finally be home after all these years to see me graduate when in actuality I wasn't even graduating from high school I had already failed every class. I begin to be depressed again not only would I be a failure to others but to my dad as well.

When I got home my mom was getting ready for church and asked me if I wanted to go. My siblings and I grew up in church going to Sunday school and bible study was a routine. Honestly, I was just going because of the treats they gave us and the field trips. I was a kid; I didn't have any problems or a reason to be focused on God like I saw my mom so focused and dependent on him. I felt like God was only for adults. Church was boring to me; I didn't know who God or Jesus was for real and the only time I prayed was when my mom made us pray together. I really wasn't up to it but for some reason I decided to tag along.

When we entered the church it was like a breath of fresh air. I was used to an all-black church where as soon as you walk in everyone is staring at you and making you uncomfortable while having on their Sunday best. Some folks were too holy that they barely spoke or smiled. This church was the complete opposite it had every race from black, white,

Haitian, Mexican etc. They all dressed casual from a suite to jeans. We walked in and everyone was smiling and welcoming, they didn't stare or give us ugly looks. We fitted right in and it wasn't forced. The music flowed through the speakers and the choir begin to sing *Lord You're Mighty* by Youthful Praise as my mom and I found our seats.

Most churches didn't allow you to sit where you felt comfortable sitting, they always had an usher to tell you where to sit. After praise and worship the pastor walked towards the pool pit and to my surprise it wasn't a man that was the pastor it was a beautiful woman of God. Her voice was soft but firm, and she had red long curly hair. She was Italian with a strong New York accent. She began to speak a word, and I was interested like never before my mind was blown away since I stepped foot inside the building. She began to talk about Moses. I was familiar with the book of Moses because growing up The Price of Egypt was always one of my favorite movies, but I never looked at the story the way the pastor put it I guess I was too young to understand. It was like she was speaking directly to me. I started to feel fire burning inside me as she spoke. Moses was a man who was running from his past. Once he found out that the person who he thought he was and the family who he thought he was born into wasn't really his family, and he had been ruling over slaves who was actually his own people caused him to have anger inside him, and he killed a man then ran away and tried to go into hiding. He changed his name and started a new family far away. Until one-night God spoke to him through a burning bush and told him he was chosen to go and let his people go from slavery. Moses was confused as to why God chose him he had just killed a man, and he was beating on his own people. Moses wasn't all that smart, and he had a stuttering problem. Moses thought people would look at him crazy, and he would be a

53

joke to think he could go and tell who he thought was his brother to let the slaves go.

The pastor said to the audience "God does not care about your past or your flaws he can still use you it's not over."

It made me realize I didn't have to be perfect for God to use me I just had to be obedient and trust him despite what it looked like. God would fight my battles for me. The Pastor said God is a promise keeper, and he is a protector, the way she put the message into words sounded like what I had been missing this whole time. A promise keeper, a protector and a father who will never leave me nor forsake me.

At the end of the service she made an announcement that if it was anybody that was willing to give their lives to Christ to meet her in the back of the church once everybody left. I was desperate and hungry for whatever God had to give me I was tired, and I had nothing to lose, so I was one of the people who stayed after service and spoke with the pastor. She gave me a bible, a notebook, and a book on how to pray.

That night I began to pray and write to God. I had so many thoughts and questions that talking to him had become an everyday thing. Nobody was forcing me this time and talking to him came naturally. I was humble enough to actually hear him and receive his message through other people, something I watched on TV, and in a dream. It blew my mind.

Every day, I would read my bible my favorite book was Matthew. I found myself falling in love with God. I had become dependent of him, I trusted in him and I put my hopes in him. From reading the word I felt like it wasn't anything I couldn't do. I felt like although I couldn't see him he was always with me. I begin to have an intimate relationship with him, I was no longer obsessed over my natural father but my spiritual father. I asked God, that if it was in his will, I would graduate high school on time with my high school diploma. I would be the first child to graduate in my home.

As time went by I begin to slowly change I wasn't fond of hanging with certain crowds anymore and I wasn't interested in certain type of man anymore. I talked different, walked different, and I even dressed different. When you get a true encounter with God you change not by accident or by force it comes naturally. I changed and I knew that I would never be the same. I knew that I wasn't perfect, but I became different. I thought different and I handled myself different. Some people didn't like it and some people did.

As I was praying for a miracle I begin to speak it out loud that I would graduate, sometimes I would tell myself that I was crazy as hell to believe I was really going to graduate, it was almost the end of my sophomore year and I still had only 3 credits when I needed a total of 24 to graduate. I didn't know how I was going to do it, but I trusted God despite what my teachers said. One thing I learned once I got into a relationship with God was, it was going to be challenging. I fought with my flesh all the time to try to do the right thing, think the right thoughts and not let people get the best of me. I thought I had to be this super holy person to please God, but I learned that God judges your heart. Even though I was still making mistakes, I still had some messed up ways and I didn't always get it right, my heart was always pure, and my intentions were always good. Having a relationship with God allowed me to feel convicted when I did something wrong I was never comfortable with the wrong-doing or making excuses. As I was fighting with my spirit and my flesh I was still attractive and still a cool chick. I began to have more guy friends than females because I just couldn't vibe with most of them, and they seem to always be in competition with each other. Me being cool with guys was an issue to some girls and the eye rolling and mean mugging started.

One day in math class a girl confronted me about her boyfriend, and I laughed in her face. I didn't take her serious because there was nothing between us. She began to pick with me with her friends in the hallway and send subliminal messages at me through social media. I was saved but I wasn't soft, so I had a trick for her. Since she wanted to start all this drama about a guy I wasn't even talking to I said fuck it and started talking to him for real. It was very easy to get his attention and that pissed her off even more.

The lunch bell rung, and I was walking the halls when I noticed the chick had changed into her gym clothes, had her hair tied up. She was walking towards me with her friends asking for a 1 on 1 fight. I laughed so hard because I just knew she couldn't be serious. I tried to remain cool and collected because my fighting days were over. I was done being that hot head girl. I tried to walk away from the situation thinking that's what God would do but before I knew it she hit me. I went from 0-100 real quick and my mind went blank.

Flashbacks of being hurt, bullied, touched and angry entered my mind. I heard voices around me saying "…stop, get off her, that's enough, she can't breathe…"

I was on top of her punching and choking her. A school guard snatched me up and I kicked her as she was still laying on the ground. The guard threw me over his shoulder and pinned me to the wall. All I remember was yelling at everybody that was surrounding the fight telling them I'll beat all they ass if they fuck with me, and I was kicking and screaming at the guard to let me go. I realized I had snapped and whatever God I had in me was gone at that moment. The guard carried me out of the hallway.

As I was sitting in the cold detention room waiting for my mom to come pick me up I started to pray because I felt bad and I couldn't believe I lashed out like that, I was doing so good. I overheard the detention teacher talking about kicking me out of school and sending me to an alternative school. I began to pray and ask for favor and to allow me to stay in school. I needed to focus and finish school. I started telling God how sorry I was.

My mom finally arrived, and I was called into the principal office. We sat at a round table and the principle spoke about how my behavior was out of the normal and when asked to stop I did not stop and because of that I was being kicked out of school and sent to an alternative school for 90 days. My mom was talking shit because I did not start the fight or hit first and demanded them to check the camera and went off about how it was very unfair that the other student was only being suspended for 5 days, and I was getting kicked out of school.

I didn't understand, I prayed to God and this was the results. I was due to go to my new school the following week. Monday morning I arrived, and it was like jail. I was used to wearing jewelry, having my nails done, cute clothes and sandals, all that was a violation. The strict dress code reminded me of visitation with my dad I felt sick as I read it.

When you get off the bus and onto the bus ramp police officers meet you at the door, and they pat you down before you are able to enter the building. I was talking shit in my head to God like you have got to be fucking kidding me. Yes I was saved, but he still wasn't through with me yet and cussing was my thing. Everything about the school gave me prison vibes and I hated it. In class students sat at a computer the whole day and worked at their own pace, there wasn't a teacher standing in front of the class teaching and participating in activities, it was every man for themselves. One of the security guards would walk around and joke at how everybody at the school has been here already and every time they would get released back to regular school they always ended up right back. He swore that I would be back, but I rebuked him, there was no way in hell I was coming back I didn't even allow myself to fit in or get comfortable. I stayed to myself and focused on my work. Sometimes I would joke around and talk bible talk to some of the students I was cool with, and they would listen. I noticed they didn't mind listening to me, and I was surprised.

This one girl stood out to me. When I would talk, she would finish my sentences, everything I was thinking she would say it out loud. It was like she was my friend mate, that's a made-up word, but it's like a soulmate. Her name was Queen she was the prettiest chocolate girl I had ever seen. We started to talk and hang out more, I had learned that we were there for the same reason and it was also her first time. The girl she fought got to stay at regular school as well. I found it so ironic it's like God brought this girl in my life at the right time. I had no friends and me and this girl just clicked. We both had the same release date, and it was coming up soon. I still needed so many credits to graduate and I wasn't sure if I wanted to return to my old school after being released. While talking to Queen she was telling me her plans and how she was enrolling into an all-girls private school that helps young girls who are struggling at home and in school. It sounded interesting, so I went home and told my mom, and we decided to try it out.

Queen and I followed each other to our new school where we were officially Best Friends. The school was a small building with 1 long hallway and a space in the middle of the building that we used as the cafeteria. It was all girls from 6th to 12th grades. I thought by it being an all-girl's school we could dress up, but we had to wear uniform shirts. School was all year we didn't get a summer and the classes was very small and also at your own pace. We had workbooks, and we had teachers who were involved. What stood out the most to me about this school was the guidance counselors. I met with my assigned counselor Ms. Betty she was the sweetest white lady with the cutest dimples. Our first meeting I thought she was going to remind me of how I was failing and how I wasn't going to graduate but instead she asked me my goals and what I was willing to do to reach them. She helped me create a vision board and asked me if it was anything she could do to help. I had never met someone so genuine; the whole school was so supportive. Not only were they about academics, but they taught us how to fill out job applications and resumes, how to dress in an interview, what to say and even how to interview others, they taught us about confidence, sex, and harassment. I learned that a lot of the girls were not like me, but we all had a story.

Most girls were homeless, living in shelters, teen moms, runaways and came from abusive homes. I loved my new school. It was then that I learned that what the devil meant for evil, God can turn it around for your good. I was right in the middle of the school year, and I was already catching up in school. My goal was to catch up on all my junior credits and go back to public school my senior year, so I could not only walk the stage and have a traditional graduation but so that I could go to prom, grad bash and whatever else regular seniors do. Life was starting to come together for me, and I was getting closer to my goals every day. Every day I would get a phone call from my dad saying he was on his way home.

Chapter 7

A Friday in September of 2011, my family and I gathered at my grandparents' house while my uncle went to pick up my dad from a prison in Coleman Florida. We all sat around nervously waiting on a day that we thought would never come. God was showing out in my life he was blessing me with everything I asked him for little by little. While the family was talking and eating dinner waiting on my dad I sat by the window the entire day looking for him. I couldn't eat or sleep, I felt myself turning into the 3-year-old me who would sit up and wait for my dad to walk through the door before I went to bed. I anticipated this day for 13 years. Now that my dad was on his way home *nothing or nobody would come between us*, I thought to myself.

Still sitting by the window I spotted my uncles black SUV pull up, my heart dropped, and I stop breathing for a minute, I couldn't believe what was happening. This dark man with long thick hair all over his body and dreadlocks in his head walked slowly from the car with the biggest smile on his face headed towards the door. The family greeted him with hugs and embraced him.

I stood froze until he grabbed me and lifted me in the air and said, "I told you I was on my way home soon Princess."

Life was now perfect. I went back to school bragging to all the girls how my dad was back. I used to dream of all the things we would do and places we would go when he finally came home. I was excited to see what he had in store for us after his release from the halfway house. When he finally got released it was nothing like I imagined, he went back to making a name in the streets getting bread., and just like before we didn't want for nothing. He got my siblings and I whatever we wanted plus more. We were able to get things my mom couldn't afford being that she was a single parent, from football gear to braces. I was bullied for having messed up teeth and I told my dad, and he promised me we would get it taken care of and he did. We didn't spend much time with him because he was always so busy getting money, and I was hurt by it. Yes, it felt good to have him home, have his protection and support but something was still missing. I wanted us to catch up on all the years that he missed out on. That's the way I pictured life once he was home, I saw us doing fun things, helping with homework and projects, and visiting theme parks. I had never been to Universal Studios or Busch gardens. I had a picture of me at Disney World when I was a year old with my dad, but I didn't remember much, so I wanted us to go back but it didn't seem like that was happening.

I was still praying and keeping my relationship with God, but I had become distant from him. Once my dad came home I felt like he was all that I was missing and needed so the talks with God and prayers became short and fast. I had my dad and it felt good but yet something inside me still felt empty, and I was feeling vulnerable and upset that I set this high expectation that my dad was not meeting at all and I didn't understand why.

While trying to focus on school and reach my goals I met this guy name Robert he was average height, brown skin with a low fade. I was attracted to the way he carried himself he was different from what I was used to. He wore polo collar shirts, khaki and nice crisp Sperry's, a very casual guy. He was 5 years older than me, had his own car, job, and apartment. I was in awe. *I see you God*, I thought to myself. He was perfect in my eyes I couldn't figure out what he wanted with my young ass who was still in school with no car or a job. He told me that it wasn't about what I didn't have it was about my mind frame of wanting it that attracted him to me. We hit it off fast he would pick me up from school, and we would hang out all day at his place.

After a month, my dad had finally met Robert one day and wasn't too fond of him at first because of his age. He said most guys who are after younger girls are manipulative and for me to be careful. He wanted to be around him more to figure him out and see what kind of agenda he had but that never happened because he was always so busy and never around much, so I continued my relationship with Robert. I was all caught up with my classes and I enrolled back into public school for my senior year like I planned. I had got so caught up that when I went back to public school I only had one elective course to do and three math classes. I hated math and was never good at it. I tried my best to avoid it, but I knew I had to find a way to pass in order to graduate. I had to take Geometry, Algebra 1 and 2 all in the same year plus pass math FCAT. I started to doubt everything I work so hard for because math just wasn't my thing. I spoke with my dad about it, and he paid for a math tutor who I met with 3 times a week. The Funny thing is my tutor was Mr. Williams my old teacher from 8th grade.

As I studied and prayed I end up passing all my classes and was ready for graduation I couldn't believe it, it hadn't hit me yet. Everything was happening so fast I was preparing myself for my senior grad bash which I was really excited about because I had never been to a theme park and prom was just a week later on my birthday. It felt like God was moving on my behalf even though I had pushed him to the side. I was grateful and thankful because if anybody would've told me that I would be where I was at the moment I would've looked at them crazy.

The day of my prom was my 18th birthday, I wore a beautiful white and black ball gown that my grandmother gave me the year before. The dress was all white with black crystals at the top where the corset hugged my petite waist. I had a sparkling crown that said Happy Birthday around my hair that was up in a bun with black gloves looking just like a princess. What was so ironic is the theme was Cinderella. I had always been in love with Cinderella, it was my birthday and prom I don't believe that it was a coincidence. God was really showing out for me. I wish I could have had that moment for life it was so special.

Robert came by the house as I was getting ready, he wore the same colors as me, we coordinated nicely in the multiple pictures we took. I thought it was so thoughtful of him to want to be a part of my prom even though he was too old to go with me. It felt wonderful to experience this moment with my dad as well, he was there telling me how beautiful I was and taking a million pictures. Everything about the night was beautiful. After prom, I wanted to go hang out with the rest of my classmates, but Robert convinced me that hanging out with him would be better so unlike my classmates who were out doing fun things after prom I was with my man.

My relationship with Robert was getting even more serious now that I was 18. I was able to stay the night over his house, and we had become closer. Everywhere you saw him I was right there on his hip; he took me everywhere with him. I was enjoying the attention, I finally realized what I was missing from my dad, attention. Robert began to give me all the attention I needed. Everything I thought my dad was going to do Robert was filling his shoes. He took me to open my first bank account, help pick out my first car, he even took me to my first Job interview. I begin to fall deeply in love with him. I felt like he was a blessing from God. He was teaching and showing me things that my parents never taught or showed me, taking me out of town on trips that my parents never took me. I was always with him; it was us against the world. The time was near for graduation, and I was so excited I didn't have a college picked out, but I used to always look into Full Sail University because I loved writing . One day God came to me in a dream and told me that I would be a screenwriter and I thought I was crazy because I didn't even know what a screenwriter was until I googled it. I had found out what it was, laughed it off and never mentioned it again.

Weeks before my graduation my grandpa begin to get really sick and was in and out of the hospital. My grandpa was the only father figure I knew, he took my siblings and I fishing, to the dog track, and picked us up from school every Friday. When we weren't with our mom we were at my grandparents' house. He made the best southern food you can name. Every time we went to visit my grandpa I would sit on his lap while he told me about Bobo, an imaginary friend he made up for us.

It was 5am, May 19th, 2013, the morning of my graduation, I was woken up by a phone call saying that my grandfather had died in his sleep. I was devastated! I was supposed to be graduating and got the worse news ever. I decided not to walk the stage because I didn't have the strength. I sent my family a text and told them how I no longer wanted to walk. Robert came by the house to convince me to walk in honor of my grandfather, but I wasn't really trying to hear what he was saying.

Five minutes later my dad walked through the door and I smiled. He was one of the reasons why I worked so hard and came this far to be able to share this moment with him. He was the only one able to convince me to get out of bed and walk the stage and receive my diploma. When I got to the huge stadium full of people looking at my class with over 500 graduates it hit me that I really did it. All the blood, sweat and tears paid off, but I didn't do this on my own I couldn't do nothing but thank and praise God If it had not been for him this wouldn't have been possible. Standing in the restroom looking in the mirror as I fixed my cap and gown I begin to cry. I just couldn't believe how far I came.

I heard the stadium clapping and cheering and it was that time. I stood nervously by the stage shaking in my heels than I heard my name through the speakers and before I knew it I was walking across the stage receiving my High School Diploma.

Walking across the stage I spotted my dad waiting for me cheering me on yelling "That's my princess! I'm so proud of you."

At that very moment time slowed down for me, and I was enjoying every minute of watching my dad and how excited he was to see me walk the stage it was priceless.

A week later my dad was arrested for violation of probation and was sentenced to a year in prison, again, I was without my dad. I was beyond disappointed. I didn't plan on ever going back to prison, I never wanted to see him in that shit hole again, but there he was...AGAIN!

Chapter 8

The adult life was getting to me, now that I was out of school I was working every day to keep money in my pockets especially now that my dad was back in prison. I was used to nice things and I needed to maintain my lifestyle. My dad helped me purchase my first car, a convertible Volkswagen Beetle that I loved. It was beige with beige leather seats. It felt good to have my own wheels. I was the youngest in the neighborhood with the top back, but I had to work hard to make sure I kept my baby. I had to pay for my own car insurance and car payment so working was all I knew.

Robert and I were still going strong and although I was at his house almost every other night I still lived with my mom, which I hated. I was 19 still sharing a room with my little sister who was 10 years younger than me. Some nights when I got off from work at 11:30pm I would be so tired and by the time I could fall asleep all 4 of my siblings were up at 6am getting ready for school being loud. My brothers were in the other room fighting every morning too. All you heard was the walls banging and them yelling at each other about whose wearing whose clothes. My little sister cried every morning because she didn't want to get up for school and my mom walked around the house screaming at everybody. I would complain to Robert about how I hated living with my mom and how tired I was of not getting rest and not having my own space.

On February 14, 2014, Robert surprised me with an apartment. I was in awe and so shocked because although I was complaining a lot about leaving my mom's house it happened so suddenly and deep inside I wasn't sure if I was actually ready. Robert had already signed the lease in his name and paid the first month's rent. Although the lease wasn't in my name I still felt obligated to share the apartment with him because he had thought about me when he moved in and to me that was sweet of him. Robert was always so thoughtful.

After looking at the one-bedroom apartment and thanking my man all day for putting me in my own place I went back home to my mom's to tell her the news. To my surprise she was not happy at all. She tried to convince me to stay but I couldn't last another night in that house. The police were always at our door looking for my brothers, I was always cleaning up behind everyone and my mom and I always bumped heads. My mom thought moving in with Robert was a bad idea, and I thought she was mad about me moving because she didn't have me to depend on anymore. My mom was single, and I was the oldest I was the one she called on when it came to making sure my siblings were good when she wasn't around. I didn't mind, but I was tired and needed a break. I felt it was time to finally leave the nest.

As I was packing up my belonging my mom was giving me this long speech about how things are going to change between me and Robert once we start living together, how I was still young and should wait until I'm able to get a place of my own instead of living with a man and how I need to focus on my future and not end up pregnant. Everything she was saying was going in one ear and out the other. I couldn't wait to decorate our place, wake up to my man every day, walk around naked and just be in my own space. I was excited.

When we finally got all moved in Robert, and I was ready to go shopping for our new place. Our first stop was the grocery store we needed to stock up on groceries because the refrigerator was empty. Roberts mom tagged along with us to the grocery store to look for stuff for the house. As we were going down each aisle I was picking out things that I thought would be easy to cook like the microwaveable dinners I saw in

Roberts fridge at his old place. I remember he would eat them, so I figured we could grab a few. As I begin to fill the cart up, he noticed some of the things and started yelling at me about how he doesn't eat microwaveable dinners or pre-cooked meals. His mom then butted in and mentioned the things she cooked every day and how he grew up eating a home cooked meal every day and how they didn't eat dinners out of the box like hamburger helper.

My feelings were hurt at the way they were downing me for grabbing things that I thought would be okay to eat on for an easy dinner. I guess I was just used to eating that way because I came from a household where we weren't picky and had to eat whatever my mom cooked because she was a single parent with a house full. Robert came from a two-parent household and his mom had been married over 20 years, so I was willing to learn from her on how to keep up my household and keep my man happy. Robert came up in a more stable home than I did, so I knew they wouldn't steer me wrong. I got everything his mom told me to get from the store and I began to learn how to cook a full-course meal for my man at least 3 times a day.

As I began to work around the house to make it feel like a home Robert would get an attitude about everything I did. He was very picky and always reminded me of everything I did wrong. I never really had an input on our new place it was always how he wanted things. We both would work all day, and I was expected to make sure a hot meal was on the table for him when he got off, but I didn't mind because I was watching his mom, and she would work long hours and go straight to the kitchen.

I loved having my own space away from my mom, but I was starting to miss being free of a lot of responsibilities that came with a man. It was like nothing I did was ever right or to his liking as soon as I got the hang of something I was being yelled at about something else I was doing wrong like ironing his clothes making sure they were creased. I would blame my mom for not teaching me things because he made me feel bad and embarrassed. Here I am thinking I'm ready to date an older guy, but I was folding under the pressure.

Living with Robert was no better than living with my mom I felt more like his child than his girlfriend. When we weren't getting along and loving on each other I was being yelled at about something I did wrong around the house. If I didn't know something he would laugh at me and call me slow. I laughed it off, but it really hurt. I didn't think I was slow, some things I simply didn't know. In my head my man was everything compared to anybody I ever dealt with. I had a full-grown man who was teaching me new things my dad never taught me, so I thought the criticism was necessary.

After a few months I had most of the house duties down packed to his liking I was cooking, cleaning and praying for my man. I would brag to my friends on the phone about having my own place with my man while they were out partying and living life. I always told myself that I wasn't missing out on anything and being home with my man kept me out of trouble. It seemed fine until Robert begin to go out with his friends, and I was left home alone. He would always tell me to hang out with his mom and sisters, so I would go chill with them, but I always felt like I didn't fit in. They always told me what I should and shouldn't be doing or looking at me crazy whenever I would be myself. I was either too loud or too goofy. Eventually I grew into the family like I did at home with Robert and as long as I was doing everything to their liking I was fine. I didn't have many friends any more everyone faded away other than Queen, and we barely hung out because we were both always busy. I had stopped going by my mom's house so much to hang out. The only action in my life was church and social media I was able to be myself on there and see what was going on outside in the world. Once I begin to be active on social media Robert didn't like it and would say I was doing too much if I posted him or us together he would yell at me and tell me that social media was full of drama and how I needed to delete it. I would delete it like he asked, but he still was on his social media accounts and I could never understand why it was okay for him to have social media and I couldn't, so I would sneak on, and he would find out and wouldn't talk to me for days. I just couldn't understand why I could never do anything right with him, I was tired of being yelled at and walking on eggshells. I so desperately wanted to go back home but my pride wouldn't let me, plus when I found out I was pregnant Roberts behavior changed.

He was no longer yelling at me or calling me names everything seemed to be perfect. We found out we were having a baby girl, and I was so excited. When my dad called from prison I told him the news and at first he didn't seem too happy, He asked me if I was sure I was ready for that type of responsibility and wanted to know how everything was going with Robert and me. When I first told him I moved out he told me I was moving too fast but whatever I decided to do he supports me as long as Robert wasn't putting his hands on me, which he wasn't. Robert never physically put his hands on me, but I never knew that it was something called verbal abuse and that he did do.

After cleaning, cooking, and working, plus being pregnant I decided to speak up for once in a while and told Robert that he had me doing all these wifely duties while shacking up with a baby on the way and that it was not of God. I felt like I was giving this man by all and I deserved to be his wife. I wanted a family, a house and to build. I begin to pray and ask God of all these things I wanted in my notebook. I even wrote out how I

wanted my wedding from every detail down to the year I
wanted to be married.

I was almost due to have the baby and my mom had thrown
me a baby shower. Everything was so nice and pretty the
theme was strawberry shortcake. It felt good to be around
family and friends and celebrate our bundle of joy I couldn't
believe I was going to be a mother. As I was mingling around
and taking pictures Robert called me over to him to take a few
pictures together. As everyone was surrounding us with their
phones out Robert got on one knee, and asked me to marry
him. I said yes. I was so shocked I was the happiest girl in the
world. My prayers were being answered I was about to be a
whole wife.

I went back to work flaunting my ring and showing it off to
everybody. Everything was perfect I was ready to meet my
unborn child.

On June 21st I Gave birth to my beautiful baby girl Rain, I had
her on Father's Day. All my life I had been searching for love
like this, I had never felt the way I felt about anybody on this
green earth the way I felt about my baby. She changed my
whole outlook on life I knew that I had to go harder for her, I
was no longer doing the bare minimum. I told myself while
lying in that hospital bed that I was going to give her the life I
never had and that was a promise.

Robert and I were back at home with the baby and everything
seem to be good I was trying to get use to a lot of things with a
newborn. I was afraid of doing it wrong. Robert was back
yelling at me and shaming me for not remembering to put
something in the baby bag when we left the house or
forgetting to grab something from the store. He made me feel
like I was less of a mother every time I would make a mistake.
His mom would come over and help along with putting her

two cents in about everything. I listened to whatever they said. The verbal abuse would come and go sometimes we were good sometimes we were bad it all depended on if I made a mistake that day.

After two months of staying home with Rain it was time for me to go back to work. I cried like a baby knowing I had to send my daughter to daycare. Robert and his mom started to complain about me helping out more with the bills and how it was time for me to find a better job. Robert's attitude had started to change when it came to paying the bills and how he handled me, so I begin to fill out job application in hopes of finding something better, so I could be able to help and not feel like a burden. In the process of me finding a job Robert was trying to talk me into moving into these low-income apartments that were newly built, and getting food stamps and cash assistance. I told him that it didn't seem right for me to be depending on the government if I had a man at home who was marrying me soon. It wasn't the life I had planned for me and my daughter I didn't want to be that girl waiting for a handout unless I was a single mother because I could do bad all by myself. He didn't like what I was saying, but I didn't care. I told myself that I wanted better for my child and I meant that.

Robert was rushing me to find another job, but I stayed still until I heard from God. Within the next month I got a call back from a job working for the state. It was exactly what I was praying for a job with good benefits for my child. Once I was hired I took my voucher for low-income assistance back to the office told my case manager I no longer needed their services. The lady looked at me crazy and asked me to have a seat. As I sat at the desk she began to look over my past case and ask me was I sure that I no longer needed the assistance. I told her yes while giving her my updated pay stubs she looked at the paper and looked at me and told me that she had been working here 15 years and nobody my age had ever came into her office ready and willing to give up government assistance. I believe that government assistance is for families who need it and need help getting on their feet. I don't think people should get comfortable depending on the government, it should only help you and push you to reach your fullest potential to where you no longer need it anymore because you took full advantage of the assistance while you create a better living for yourself. I refused to be a slave to the government or to stay in the same predicament. I needed more and wanted more, and I was determined to get it.

One night while sleeping God spoke to me in a dream telling me it was time for me to leave our one-bedroom apartment and go back home with my mom. I ignored God and thought he was crazy to think that I was going to leave my own space to go back home to my mother especially with a baby. As the months went by and I continue to run from God and be disobedient, Robert came home to tell me how it was time to renew the lease and how rent was going up, and we needed a two-bedroom and how we could no longer stay in our one-bedroom with rain. After searching and searching to find a cheaper place to stay with two bedrooms it seems like everywhere we went was more expensive and I refused to pay expensive rent when I knew I could get a home if I put my mind to it. Like always God has a way of getting my attention and this was it. I could no longer run from God and I decided to pack up my things and move back home with my mom. At first Robert didn't agree but once he saw I was serious we both decided to move back with our parents. We talked about saving to purchase a home and to save all our money for a year while we both lived with our parents and took turns with the baby.

Nothing about living with my mom had changed other than it was a bit quieter because my brothers were always running the streets and my mom was still never home. Robert, and I was managing going back and forth with the baby, it was easy because his parents lived not even five minutes from my mom. Despite us not being under the same roof as a family I didn't mind the little freedom I was getting of not having to walk on eggshells.

Chapter 9

My dad was finally back home, and I felt like a big weight was lifted off my shoulder I was starting to be concerned about my brothers they had gotten out of control from hanging with the wrong people, skipping school and getting arrested especially David. Now that my dad was home for the second time it seems like he was more focused on spending time with us then getting money and in the streets. When he saw his granddaughter for the first time he fell in love. I saw a twinkle in his eye, something had changed about him, and I liked it. This is what I had been waiting and praying for.

David's behavior had gotten worse, he was in and out of the detention center every week. My dad decided to move David in with him and his girlfriend so that he could keep him out of trouble and guide him the right way. It was good seeing my dad bond with his sons and trying to get them to do the right thing. It was almost pointless trying to tell them through jail calls not to run the streets.

My dad had us all together hanging out more often and taking trips. He loved being a grandad, he spoiled Rain rotten and it was refreshing to see him babysit her and love on her because it reminded me of our relationship. My dad was also able to bond with Robert, and they ended up being closer than I thought. He loved and respected Robert and that made me feel like I made the right decision. My dad didn't know what went on personally in our relationship but from the outside looking in he supported us 100%.

The verbal abuse no longer bothered me now that my dad was back around because he was the complete opposite of Robert. While I was walking on eggshells and being yelled at by my Husband, my dad never raised his voice at me, he never called me out my name and if I didn't understand something he didn't treat me as if I was dumb. My dad was a sweet escape from the reality of what I had to deal with. I found myself always comparing them and if Robert didn't do something I wanted, I would just ask my dad.

Robert spoiled me but it was never enough. I realized it would never be enough because when I met Robert I was looking for a fatherly love and now that I had my father back what did I need him for? I was in love with him, my daughter needed him, and I wanted to give her the life that I never had which is why it was important to me to marry him and try to build a foundation.

Meanwhile, my dad had found another way of getting money, it wasn't legit, but it wasn't what he was doing before, and it became a big thing, and he was the plug when it came to football picks and gambling. He would lose money, but when he hit; it was big. His new hobby had him busy and David was drifting back to his bad behavior. He was causing more trouble with the law and my dad didn't want that type of traffic where he lived so David came back home to our moms.

Early one Friday morning I was up getting Rain ready for her six-month shots. Robert was on his way to bring us to the Doctor. David woke up that morning, peeked his head in my room door and asked to see his niece. He played with her and kissed her and headed for the living room to play the PS4 like every other morning. Thirty minutes later Robert had made it to the house and David left to hang with his friends in our grandparent's neighborhood.

Robert and I were headed to our appointment when my grandma called me screaming through the phone that David had been shot. I stopped in the middle of ongoing traffic and begin to shake and tremble. Robert was yelling trying to figure out what the hell was going on and how I was about to kill us by sitting in the middle of traffic. I looked him in the eyes with tears going down my face and told him David had been shot, and we needed to go to the hospital. He jumped in the driver side and speed to the hospital running through every light. We forgot we had the baby in the car.

At the hospital outside the emergency entrance where the rest of the family was waiting to hear an update I begin to pray. I called my dad, but his phone was going straight to voicemail. I watched my mom scream and cry and Robert held me in his arms. At just 16 years old my brother was shot to death.

My dad called back.

"Did he make it?" he asked with tears in his voice.

"No." I replied. He hung up without saying a word.

I went home feeling in denial, this couldn't be my life. I found myself asking God why when everything was starting to come together for me did something bad have to happen. Is this why God kept me up at night telling me to go back home with my mom because now she needs me like never before. I had distanced myself from my family but I'm so glad I was able to come back home and spend time with my brother because I never thought in a million years that I would lose him. I'd much rather have visited him in a program then the grave. He was too young he still had his life to live, mistakes to make and things to learn this just wasn't fair.

Rumors began circulating about my brother's death and my dad begin to act weird and distant, he wasn't the same. Robert felt like my mom's house wasn't safe for me and the baby, so he moved us in with his parents. I thanked God for him, this had been his 2nd time he had to watch me mourn the loss of someone close to me, and he was always supportive…he would always start off supportive, and then he would go back to his controlling ways, now that I was living with his parents it was worse. I begin to become more distance from my family again because he thought it wasn't safe for us and that I needed to choose between the family I was creating and the family I came from.

I felt like Robert didn't understand that seeing my brother lay in that casket made me want to be closer to my remaining relatives. it just didn't feel right building this family while my blood was hurting and lost. I still had other brothers that was in the streets that I felt like I had to save but Robert always reminded me that he and my daughter were more important and that I couldn't save them if they didn't want to listen. I looked at my daughter as I sat in another family's house that wasn't mine and told myself that I had to give her better and Robert was right I needed to focus on the family I was creating.

I begin to focus on us being homeowners. It was so hard to have goals in a house full of dream killers, every time I looked for reasons why it would work, Robert would look for reasons why it wouldn't. I found out about a homeowner's program through my mom and decided to try it out. Robert got on board and we begin the process. After getting approved and finding a house Robert and his parents did not agree that it was the house for us. I had prayed and asked God for guidance and this is where he led me, and they were discouraging me. I needed Robert to have my back and believe that this was our house, but he spent too much time thinking of every negative thing about what I was trying to build for our future. I begin to ignore the negative energy that was starting to consume me and focus on what God promised me.

In less than 90 days I was closing on my first home! I was in disbelief. I was 21, engaged and building for my family. I learned that when God has something for you, and he says yes it doesn't matter what people around you say no, even if it's your own significant other. Now that I was building this foundation I was ready to get settled in with my family. It was time to start planning the wedding. I was so excited I had been dreaming of my wedding since a little girl. I had the whole thing planned from the colors, to the theme and decorations. It felt so good to talk with my dad about my big day. I was happy to share this moment with him. My mom did not agree with me marrying Robert she didn't think he was the one for me and thought I was making a big mistake. My dad and Robert said that my mom was just jealous and to do what made me happy.

My mom and I became even more distant as the wedding day got closer. I sat on the phone with Queen, who I asked to be my maid of honor, and talked about all my wedding plans until she began to distant herself as well. I was trying to figure out why everyone was acting funny now that I was getting married. Robert convinced me that they were just jealous of me and I didn't need them long as I had him. I continued to plan my wedding and it came natural because I had just started an event planning business. I didn't get much support from my side of the family other than my dad, but Roberts family was very supportive.

I was sad that the closest friend I had decided not to be in my wedding anymore and my mom was giving me a hard time, nothing about getting married felt special anymore. Robert and his family told me that when you decide to want better for your life people change and that's what was happening. They told me that women wished they had a man to love them and marry them and not to worry because they would always support me no matter what. I was thankful but I wanted my own mother and my own friends who I could be myself with. I was tired of being in the shadow of Robert and his family, but I figured this was how it was supposed to be and proceeded with my wedding. I was down to three bridesmaids: Robert's sister, my God sister and a close friend from high school. I had all of my decorations ready for my big day but nobody to get the job done because the one person who I depended on, who knew exactly how I wanted my dream wedding was not supportive, and that was my mom.

I was stressed out and depressed about a day that I thought was supposed to be magical. Things begin to get worse with Robert and he started coming home late, hanging out more and always in his man cave on the phone. We had sex less because every time we had sex I ended up at the Doctor and I couldn't figure out why. My intuition was telling me something was up so I asked him if we could go to counseling before the wedding. He said no, we didn't need anybody in our business. I left it alone and continued planning for the wedding. The more distant he got the lonelier I was. I needed someone to talk to. I met this guy at work who I begin to talk to and vent to. I knew talking to him was wrong, but it felt good. I kept it to communication only, we never had sex he was my getaway when I couldn't talk to Robert. I had never cheated, and I wasn't planning to.

It was 3am on a Monday when my mom called me crying through the phone, she said that Federal Agents surrounded her house and arrested my little brother Tyrone for racketeering. His bond had been set at 1 million dollars. There I was in the middle of planning a wedding and getting the worst news since David had been killed. I couldn't eat or sleep for days, I stayed up worried about losing another brother. Robert told me not to worry and to focus on the family we were building, so I prayed day in and out for my brother as I planned my own wedding. It hurt that two of my brothers wouldn't be there on my special day, but I had to work with what I had.

October 28, 2017, on David's birthday I married the love of my life. Although my mom did not feel like I should be marrying Robert, at the last minute she decided to come to the wedding and did my wedding decor just the way I dreamed she would.

The room was dripped in champagne gold, gold and ivory. The tables were ivory with gold and every other table had sparkling pumpkins with a gold carriage as centerpieces surrounded by gold antique candleholders holding ivory candles with gold floating rose candles that lit the whole room up. Each table had gold picture frames with our engagement photos inside. Upon entering the venue there was a gold antique mirror that read Once upon a time.

The venue was surrounded by oak trees with moss. Due to the weather we had everything inside which was still beautiful. The inside had windows wrapped around the room looking out at the trees that looked like walking into an enchanted Forrest. My two-tiered ivory cake sat in the middle of the room on top of a gold sequin tablecloth, with a gold topper read Happily Ever After. The altar was draped in gold and ivory with pumpkins going down the aisle. Each chair was covered in white with our wedding program made out of antique parchment paper on each seat.

The dress code for the guest was ivory, my bridesmaids wore sleeveless ivory mermaid dresses that were covered in taupe lace, which complimented the groomsmen who were dressed in all ivory with an ivory and gold designed vest. The whole bridal party was elegantly dipped in gold and ivory. Then there was me, the bride, in a gold Cinderella ball gown. The corset and the bottom of the dress was embellished with gold and silver crystals. The dress was a two piece where the skirt detached from the corset and turned into a sexy tight fitted pencil skirt. I had gold bedazzled heels that matched my dress. My hair was up in a high bun that sat in the center of a gold crown. The gold complimented my brown skin and my makeup that was naturally and beautifully done. Rain who was the flower girl matched me, we had the same gold dress she was a mini me, and I was proud to finally be giving her a life I never had.

As the wedding party began walking, I exited the dressing room to meet my father who was so fly in his gold and ivory. He looked so handsome and young, like he could be my brother. When our eyes connected I saw tears and all 32 of his teeth smiling at me.

He told me I was the most beautiful girl in the world. I was so nervous that I had to pee he started laughing.

"You sure you ready for this?" He asked.

"Yes."

I heard *Vows* by Jamie Foxx play through the speakers as I walked side by side, holding my dad as he walked me down the aisle.

I saw my soon-to-be husband standing at the altar drunk. I was disgusted but I kept my composure. Everything was beautiful, and I was happy to see my family together in good spirits and that made me happy. I wasn't going to let Robert being drunk ruin this night. The pastor announced us Mr. & Mrs. Anderson we were married. I was officially a wife. I actually thought I had my happily ever after.

Chapter 10

Robert and I never had a honeymoon stage, after we said I DO our relationship got worse.

We became strangers.

I woke up one day and had no idea who this guy was that I married. Everything that my intuition was telling me before we got married had started to reveal now that we were official. He had been cheating the whole time and was even laid up with another woman the night before our wedding. I knew something was up the whole time, but I ignored it.

I wanted my family to work, so I begged for us to go to counseling but again he refused. He then tried to make me feel guilty about talking to someone else knowing he was out doing me dirty. I swallowed my fears and remained by his side, but it got worse once he began to have problems at work, he would bring them home and the yelling began, it got so bad that it was putting a toll on our child and others around us. Most of the time he didn't want to be bothered he just isolated himself from us. I was trying my best to be supportive when he complained about work, but it was starting to be exhausting, so I recommended that he figured out a plan to get his self out of this situation so that our home can be peaceful, but I realized that the man I married didn't have any drive or goals, he was content. I had goals and dreams that I tried to push on him and that started to irritate both of us.

I realized that I was outgrowing my husband, yet I still was trying to force my marriage to work. I loved this man with my whole heart. He wasn't perfect, but he had some great qualities, he was hard-working, supportive, and family oriented he always put his household first, but that just wasn't enough for me. I wanted more out of life, I wanted to do more and see more, but we weren't on the same page. We weren't a couple, we were roommates! I was distant from God, so I decided to get back intimate with him because I knew the power of prayer. I found myself filling up Roberts cup, but I was running empty he wasn't filling me up yes he was physically there, but I needed someone to pray with me when I didn't have the words, someone to tell me everything was going to be okay. I was mentally drained from my shitty marriage to my brother fighting for his life in jail. Every time I turned the TV on he was the headline, facing up to 30 years.

My dad had changed drastically since the death of David and it was hard to get through to him sometimes. He didn't take the death of his son well; I could tell he wasn't himself and now he was even more stressed from lawyer fees trying to make sure his other son's life wasn't taken from the system. It was like my family just couldn't catch a break. At work, it was hard for me to focus because I had so much going on in my life.

Strange things started to go on with my dad; he had switched up vehicles and I started hearing from him more but seeing him less, so I was really out of it because I couldn't seem to get through to any of the men in my life. My dad began telling us to watch our surroundings, shortly after I started noticing weird things like being followed by strange cars. Strange men would come into my job just to watch me. I no longer felt safe so human resources isolated me from the public eye and moved me to an office behind the scenes to work. I felt like my family's life was in danger again, which stressed me out even more. I didn't know who to talk to or who to trust.

I was scrolling through FB when I ran across a profile picture that looked like Eric. My heart dropped I started to feel like it was God sending me a sign to give myself closure. I never realized how the situation still affected me until I saw his face. I swallowed hard and messaged praying it was a fake page. When I messaged him one of his family members replied and agreed to relay the messages back and forth until we were able to speak on the phone because we both didn't trust each other. The last time we spoke he was telling me the baby wasn't his and to fuck off. The last time we saw each other was in court for his sentencing.

When we finally spoke I explained to him that I wasn't that young girl anymore and I can speak for myself now. I apologized to him for what he possibly had to go through while in jail from other inmates due to the crime, and he apologized for the role he played but for some reason his apology didn't seem sincere, I didn't believe that he was really sorry or felt that he did anything wrong. I only wanted closure for myself to get the hate out of my heart that I had for him for being bullied and leaving me for dead while being pregnant and manipulating me. With so much going on in my life the conversations turned into an everyday thing, and I found myself enjoying the company. He really had me feeling like he was going to finally admit I never lied to him about my age and that prison had changed him. I came to him with a pure heart I even told him I would clear his name from the rape accusations because he felt like my dad still thought it was true although I said it wasn't in mediation. He explained how he had been trying to reach out to my dad and apologize, but he would never respond. I really thought we both were putting all this behind us until he spazzed out on me. He turned it all around on me, again, and asked for me to help him get out because he didn't do anything. I realized that talking to him wasn't a good idea. This man was trying to mindfuck me, and I was falling for it. I decided not to answer my phone for him anymore because he wasn't genuine, and I wasn't allowing him to manipulate me again. Although I stop speaking to him, I still spoke to my dad about it which was very hard for me, I prayed about it for days until I got confirmation. When I finally built the nerve to speak to my dad I told him how I forgave Eric and how he should too. I explained that this incident was a big thing for me and it's crazy how it's a trend now and nobody sees the wrong in it, which is sad. Older dudes talking to girls that are young enough to be their daughter was normal even my dad wasn't tripping on it. I didn't feel like it was okay, and I was being dragged for it. I realized that people pick and choose what's wrong and right until it happens to them or someone close to them and God doesn't work like that. How can you expect God to show you grace and mercy, but he isn't allowed to show that same grace and mercy to others? After a long talk with my dad he was supportive as always, and I was at peace with it and could close that chapter for good. I learned forgiving a person and getting closure isn't always about the other person sometimes it's about you.

Eric wasn't ready to accept his wrongdoing and I wasn't about to force it on him or allow him to use reverse physiology on me. I wasn't allowing nothing or nobody from my past to control my future. I closed that chapter and moved on I pray that one day he can too.

In September of 2018, my brother's case was scheduled for trial and by the grace of God all charges were dropped! My family was happy, we were finally at peace and could get some rest. It was time to celebrate, my dad was very serious about us finally getting together and taking family portraits, and we did. They came out beautiful everything was slowly going back to normal right before the holidays, so I thought.

November 27th, 2018 I woke up that morning and FaceTime my dad like I do every morning before work. Work was ok that day and I sat on the phone with my dad for a whole hour on my lunch break which was not normal for us. My dad was always busy and never talked on the phone more than fifteen minutes, but on this day he seemed so calm and collected. He wasn't out handling business like the usual, he was home relaxing and enjoying the day. He told me he wasn't going to leave the house that day and he was just going to chill until later and then drive out of town to visit my brother in college. We talked about my business ideas, investing and how I was such a Daddy's girl. He laughed at how I was his weakness, and could get him to do almost anything, and how he could never tell me no. We laughed so hard on the phone he didn't even want to hang up, but I told him I would talk to him later because my break was over, we said I love you and the phone hung up.

That evening I got off of work and headed home to prepare dinner like usual. I had a long drive home and for some reason I was feeling really uneasy and my heart started to ache, like chest pains. but I didn't know why . My intuition told me to call my dad, but I told myself once I got home and finish dinner I would call him back. I made it home and begin cooking dinner my phone started ringing off the hook.

I answered and heard screaming causing me to drop my phone. My husband ran in the kitchen and asked me what was wrong, and for a long minute I couldn't speak it was like I couldn't breathe my heart had stopped.

Once I caught my breath I told him that we needed to go to the hospital because my dad had been shot in a drive by and wrecked into a power line just a block from where my brother was killed. The whole neighborhood had lost power. As Robert rushed to get him and the baby dressed I felt myself having what I thought was a mini heart attack. On our way to the hospital my heart kept racing to what seemed like 1000 beats a second, then it would slow down, it kept this same rhythm all the way to the hospital then it stopped completely.

Something didn't feel right, this was different. I heard my husband screaming for me to breath and relax, it was like my heart was outside of my body. I was there but I wasn't.

Once inside the hospital with the rest of our family and friends we sat and waited for what seemed like hours. The Gang unit was posted outside waiting as well. When the Doctor came out with an officer and pulled my brother and grandfather to the side to speak with them privately I began to feel dizzy. I seen my brother walk back from around the corner with tears in his eyes and I fell out and hit the ground. That was all the confirmation I needed because the last time I seen my brother cry was at our brothers funeral. All I kept hearing was the little girl inside of me crying out for her daddy over and over and over and over again.

He was gone my daddy was gone again and this time he wasn't coming back . If God had never put anything on me that I couldn't bear, this was the something I couldn't bear, this was something I couldn't accept it had to be my time to go because I couldn't live any longer. It was like someone took a chainsaw and pressed it into my heart because it was torn into pieces and there was no repairing it.

While everyone left the hospital after the news I sat in the waiting room waiting to see him. I wanted to see him, touch him, kiss him. He was all alone nobody stayed to even identify his body, I was out of it. Robert asked me if I was sure I wanted to see my dad that way he was afraid that I would be traumatized and deep down inside I felt that way too, so I walked back to the car in the daze.

I was mad at everybody I was mad at the world and I definitely was mad at God. The closest people to him switched up on him before he was even in the dirt. My heart was full of rage when I heard my grandma say *life goes on* and it hadn't even been 24 hours of him being gone. Things were being taken from his house before my brothers and I had a chance to even get to process what the fuck was happening. Everybody became money hungry and was stealing from him. How can a man who took care of everybody and cared about everybody be treated like shit once he took his last breath? His own mother didn't want to give him the proper burial he deserved.

I found myself asking people for help just to bury him because money was stolen out of his house and his life insurance policy was denied. I was sick to my stomach when my uncle told me not to waste money on buying him a nice suite for his burial. He said to bury him in the same suite he gave me away in. It was disgusting the way I watched family move funny over money. I was an event planner but never in my life did I think I would be planning my own father's funeral I don't even know how I did it.

I remember sitting in the office at the funeral home as she showed me multiple styles of caskets to choose from and I felt like throwing up. Robert and I went shopping to choose my dad's very last outfit and to make sure he looked good and spodie like the man he was. I wasn't going to let my father leave this earth any kind of way. I didn't play about my dad. The love I had for my dad was real and deep...maybe too deep.

Chapter 11

As I walked slowly down the aisle, looking at the white casket trimmed in gold, everything became a blur. It all seemed surreal. I'm sure everyone was expecting me to be weak, falling out crying, yelling, and screaming like most people do at funerals but I didn't do any of that. I looked down inside the casket and seen how handsome my dad was with his long thick dreadlocks freshly twisted hanging in front of him. He was dressed *spodie* in a white Michael Kors shirt from Mens Warehouse with some white slacks, a brown Gucci scarf around his neck with his Gucci belt on. He looked good.

I stood and stared at him for a few minutes then I leaned over and whispered in his ear.

"I got you. I promise."

I gently kissed his cold lips and then took a seat in the front row and watched more people walk in approaching the casket. So many screams and cries filled the church, but I tuned it all out as I reflected on the day I got the call that he had just been murdered. I sat in the front row feeling defeated and fed up. No matter how much I leaned on God and did right in life me or my family just couldn't catch a break. I closed my eyes in the midst of the choir singing *For Your Glory* by Tasha Cobb and I began to go back to the earlier years in my life trying to figure out what I did that was so wrong because I felt like karma was kicking my ass. I didn't know what God was doing but it felt like I was being punished for being a Daddy's girl.

After the funeral everyone headed to the burial, but that was something I didn't have the strength to do. I refused to watch my daddy get put into the ground, so I stayed in the limousine while the rest of the family got out. When we left the cemetery

I felt my heart leave my body. The old April died and was buried with her daddy. I told myself I was never going back to the cemetery I figured if I could pretend he was in prison I would be able to move on with my life. I no longer wanted to deal with my family. I was hurting and I didn't want anyone seeing me at my weakest I was used to being the strong one.

Chapter 12

I never had time to grieve. Between my family and my marriage I was told… life goes on. I was dying on the inside. Robert needed sex, my brothers needed support and my daughter wanted her grandfather. As for me it was fuck everybody. Fuck the marriage I was no longer putting up with cheating and being mentally drained, it was fuck family because they showed me that family changes when money is involved. I didn't trust or want to deal with anyone. When I went back to work I didn't feel welcomed, everybody was staring and watching me trying to see who I really was. Every time you turned on the news all you saw was my family. These people at work looked at me as a threat. I didn't feel like I belonged anywhere not at home or at work. I was lost I didn't know who I was anymore I was broken, hurt, bitter & vulnerable.

As soon as I looked through my dad's paperwork from the hospital and the police report from that night I regret reading it. It made things worse for me. The hospital report described everything he went through as he was fighting for his life, in detail. What stood out to me the most was the rhythm of his heart beating . It was the same rhythm as my heart that night when I was on my way to the hospital. I got chills through my body as I read how our hearts beat the same.

A father is oftentimes a little girls first love and if you've never had a father or you lose a father it can be just like losing the love of your life, even more if your father never showed you what love is, or how it's supposed to feel, it's a feeling that you'll always yearn for.

After reading the reports I knew I needed to seek help I just didn't know how or from whom, so I did what I knew best and

95

that was to pray. I begin to pray Robert out of my life right up until he left. I no longer wanted the marriage; we weren't good for each other.

When you pray for things you have to make sure you're ready for it because I no longer wanted Robert, but I also didn't want to let him go . Robert was all the man I knew and the only one I had left. He was like a father figure to me, letting go was hard. I found myself going back because I didn't know how to be alone. I felt like I needed to have someone, and I was willing to risk my happiness, freedom, and peace just so I wouldn't be alone. It was hard but I was trying and slowly I was able to get away.

Once I was away I got even more vulnerable. I was in search of something, but I didn't know what it was. One of my dad's closest friend name Pablo called me one night to check on me and we talked on the phone for hours about everything but mainly about me and what I was going through. Talking to Pablo became a routine. Every morning he would text me things like, *get up let's get this money*. He reminded me so much of my dad the way he spoke. We would talk and text all day and night. He had a way with his words and that kept me so in tuned with him. He was so full of knowledge and his voice was deep and mellow.

Pablo was attracted to me I could tell the way he looked at me but neither one of us was going to make the first move because that was my dad's friend. Pablo knew what I was going through with my marriage and he gave me a lot of advice. He never mentioned anything about having a girlfriend the whole time we talked . It wasn't until after he invited me out for drinks one night that I got a phone call from a woman asking me what was going on between us . I felt betrayed because why was this man calling and texting me all day and night and not once did he mention to me that he was in a relationship. Yes he was my dad's friend, but I never hung around any of his friends long enough to know their personal life it was only 1 guy who I was around and called uncle and that was my dad's best friend, and he didn't call him friend he called him bro.

Pablo and I weren't dating or anything, but I felt like he owed me an explanation because this was someone I expressed my whole life to and he had been having fights at home with his girl about me, and I had no clue about. The girl and I talked on the phone for hours and I was hurt because I had caught feelings for this man. How could I be so damn dumb and naïve? When I confronted him it didn't go the way I thought it would go.

We were all over each other. I was sleeping with someone who was close to my dad. *How could I be so nasty?* I needed to end this but didn't know how. It wasn't until I found out more about him, like how he was sweet-talking me but at home beating his girl's ass. I was sleeping with a monster I was so disgusted. I ended things with him and immediately went to seek help.

I walked into the Doctors office and sat down on the couch. There was a sweet aroma I smelled as soft music was played. I was greeted by a short African American lady with long hair and big eyes. She was very soft-spoken, and her breath smelled like peppermint. As I sat across from her I was thinking to myself what the hell was I doing there talking to a complete stranger.

What do I even say to this woman where do I even start? The first session was hard because she didn't talk or ask me anything other than for me to tell her how I was feeling. After going to a few more sessions it started to become harder for me she was making me face things I didn't want to face so I stopped going.

The more I was alone the more I had to control my thoughts and work on myself. I started to notice toxic things about myself that I didn't like. I felt I was being hard up for a man, it was like I needed a man so bad when really I didn't. I needed to learn how to find and love myself. I was learning new things about myself slowly but surely. Multiple men were coming at me. Pablo wasn't the only guy who had tried to ease his way on to me after my dad passed. So many men were hitting me up saying how they were sorry for my lost and how if I ever needed anything to hit them up but were really trying to get with me. I didn't understand why these men wanted me. Was it because of my dad? They never looked my way when he was living now they were in-line waiting like kids at a candy store, but they weren't kids. For a young girl it wasn't a good feeling.

Months later I ran into this guy name lil Don. He was around my age, handsome, well-groomed and very laid back. He chased me for weeks before I gave in. I liked him because he was consistent. I noticed he was about his money and wasn't flashy just like my dad. After Robert left I was stuck paying all the bills on my own, so having a man around who didn't mind helping me out was a blessing. I was struggling and had to pick up a second job while Robert was home with his parents making more money than me with less bills. I would ask him for help, but he would say no and that I wanted him out, so he wasn't obligated to help pay my bills, so I put my big girl pants on and made shit happen for me and my child. She needed a roof over her head while she was with me, food, lights and other necessities.

Lil Don was a big help; he would give me money all the time without me asking and was always supporting everything I did. He reminded me so much of my dad. I began to let him stash his drugs in my home and I would watch him as he prepared it. I had gone from a wife to a drug dealer's girl. Don't get me wrong it was fun and exciting at first, but he started coming with a lot of drama that I had no idea about. It was like a horrible cycle I couldn't break.

A girl called my phone telling me how she was lil Don's girl but only this time I wasn't leaving, she was gonna have to share him. I had watched my dad take care of two women and two different households and it seem like it worked out pretty good to me. I hung up the phone and continued with my relationship with Don. He was spoiling me the same way my dad did. Every little thing my heart desired I got it. I wasn't stupid enough to quit my second job though. I didn't give a damn how much money a man was bringing in I was taking my ass to work.

Soon being Don's girl became a competition, now that his other girl knew about me I started seeing him less and we were always was arguing. He started being careless with his products around the house and I just couldn't take the lifestyle anymore, so I left. I was back at square one when it came to men. I decided to discipline myself and focus on healing. I was chasing after my dad in all these different men and this wasn't the life I wanted for myself I was better than this and I wanted to be a good example for my daughter and little sister.

I went back to counseling and in the beginning it caused me to be more depressed because I had to go back and dig deep from within. I couldn't concentrate at work, I started to lose focus. Healing had cost me my job. On March 17, 2020 I got fired.

Covid-19 had just surfaced so no other jobs were hiring. I was stuck with my part time job making $10 a hour trying to figure out my next move. My life couldn't get any worse than it already was. As I sat home with nothing do I continued to seek the help I needed from my counselor and I was able to take the time I had to heal and take care of myself.

When I lost my dad I lost myself, I didn't know who I was anymore, and when I finally found myself again, I wasn't the April people were used to, this time I had to leave my dad behind. I could no longer obsess with being a daddy's girl, or the idea of having him around; he was gone. I now depend on my spiritual father. I'm allowing God to love me, heal me and take care of me. I'm not choosing men based on daddy issues anymore!

God is a jealous God and did not approve of the way I worshipped my dad as if he was a God. Loosing my dad ended up being the best thing that happened to me because when I lost him, I found myself.

I finally built the courage to visit my dad's grave and that was the day I let him go. I needed to so I could live my life without being vulnerable, taken advantage of and looking for love in all the wrong places. I take full accountability for the choices I've made throughout my journey, but this is my story, my truth, real, raw & uncut. I will always be a daddy's girl no matter what, but my grandma was right in the beginning. Life goes on.

About the Author

Natori Pitts was born and raised in Fort Myers, Florida. After graduating from high school, she began working to provide for her daughter, but she always knew she wanted more. She became an entrepreneur at 21 years old as an event planner and CEO of Dezinate Event Planning LLC. Natori found her gift in writing when she started communicating with God in prayer and writing all her goals down in a notebook. Writing has healed her in many ways, and she hopes that her story will help to heal others as well.

Follow the Author...

- ✓ **Facebook:** Natori Pitts
- ✓ **Instagram:** Natori Jazmine
- ✓ **Twitter:** Natori Pitts
- ✓ **YouTube:** DaddysGirl TheBook

Made in the USA
Columbia, SC
03 February 2021